THE GREAT
AMERICAN FOREST

THE GREAT

Illustrations by STANLEY WYATT

AMERICAN FOREST

by RUTHERFORD PLATT

PRENTICE-HALL, INC., Englewood Cliffs, N. J.

The Great American Forest
by Rutherford Platt

Library of Congress Catalog Card Number: 65-25253

Printed in the United States of America
T36353

Prentice-Hall International, Inc., London
Prentice-Hall of Australia, Pty., Ltd., Sydney
Prentice-Hall of Canada, Ltd., Toronto
Prentice-Hall of India (Private) Ltd., New Delhi
Prentice-Hall of Japan, Inc., Tokyo

Dedicated
to
Mac and Miriam

Other books by Rutherford Platt

This Green World
Our Flowering World
The Woods of Time
American Trees, A Book of Discovery
Pocket Guide to Trees
Wilderness, The Discovery of a Continent of Wonder
The River of Life
1001 Questions Answered About Trees
Worlds of Nature
Secrets of Life
Adventures in the Wilderness
   with Horace Albright

THE history of the human race has always been related to—and sometimes dominated by—the history of forests. Even the larger mammals could not begin to inherit the earth until, less than fifty million years ago, with the cooling climate, the hardwood trees began to flourish. And this occurrence provoked one of the greatest crises in the history of man himself, when toward the end of the last great ice age the spread of forests over what had been a sub-arctic plain forced a whole new way of life upon homo sapiens.

The majority of men in Europe and America lead lives which seem to them almost completely isolated from the forces of nature, and they are likely to be ignorant of the value and of even the existence of forests. Yet today forests cover about 664 million acres of the continental United States and account for more than thirty per cent of its total area. In Great Britain, on the other hand, they occupy only four percent of its land.

In both countries they were, of course, once far more extensive, and the difference between the two figures is a very rough measure of the length of time each country has been inhabited by men increasingly capable of profoundly modifying the physical world they inhabit. Forests are now more and more dependent upon the tolerance of the creature they formerly threatened. Once they were something to be conquered; now they are, in the minds of a thoughtful minority, something to be saved. And the moment at which the balance shifts is a result of the length of time that civilized man has been attempting to impose his will upon a land. To Caesar's legions, accustomed to a long-tamed Italy, the great forests of Germany were a terror. Not much more than a millennium and a half later Englishmen were beginning to be seriously concerned about the possible exhaustion of timber, although at almost the same moment most newcomers to the American continent were, like Caesar's legions, terrified of the forest and concerned with nothing except the clearing of it.

Two Europeans, André and François Michaux, did realize that the New World represented something which had vanished from Europe forever and they came to America early in the nineteenth century to describe it in *The North American Sylva*. But it was not until about a century later that even a minority of Americans began to realize that forests were something which ought to be saved from destruction. It is logical but also startling that a century ago anything referred to as a Wilderness Bill would have been naturally assumed to be something aimed at conquering rather than preserving our forests.

Rutherford Platt's fascinating fact-filled book is concerned with the various aspects of one-third of the United States. It describes what forests are, how they live and develop, where the different kinds occur, what they do and what is done to them—in short it introduces the reader to a dwindling and threatened part of America, which is materially and spiritually important; a part of America which has been energetically exploited, often shamefully abused, but little understood. It is, therefore, a most fitting first volume in a series dealing with our natural world.

—Joseph Wood Krutch

Contents

THE GREAT
AMERICAN FOREST

chapter one

Wilderness Traces

NORTHWESTERN Minnesota is peppered with lakes which are in fact puddles left over where the area was plowed by glaciers and then piled up with sediments by roaring torrents from the south-facing cliffs of the retreating ice.

About three miles north of Pelican Falls, Route 50 cuts through a river embankment where the excavation is deeper than elsewhere, exposing ancient solid clay that underlies the glacial till—a loose mixture of gravel and small boulders, which must be excavated deeply to make a firm foundation for a road. A workman, straightening this cut, was pecking away at its side with a pickax when a bony hand thrust out from the clay and seemed to beckon to him, as if somebody buried there were signaling for help. He called out to fellow laborers to come and see. The road builders, filled with curiosity and much amused, gingerly unearthed the skeleton of a body that had been encased there in the clay, well below the surface of the ground. In the words of delighted archeologists who later described the find, "The workmen who uncovered it gave it intelligent care."

Human skulls are the most telltale clue by which archeologists conjure up the people of the silent past. They reveal the human type, but usually not the sex. In the idiom of archeology such an exhibit is a "man." In this case, the whole skeleton was found, unshattered by time or bull-

3

dozers. It was, beyond doubt, the skeleton of a girl about fifteen years old, whose label in the file reads "Minnesota Man."

A careful search of the place brought to light no other bones of beast or man. Minnesota Man was apparently alone when she died, and somehow her body was undiscovered and left undisturbed by both friends and wild animals. On thongs around her neck she wore two graceful articles —a slender dagger such as a young girl might own, carved from the tine of an elk's antler, and a spiraling conch shell which may have been used as a horn or whistle or merely as a piece of costume jewelry. Both were perforated for stringing.

The most striking features of Minnesota Man were her thrusting jaw and large teeth, the narrowness of the skull and its long extension backward. These are very primitive human features, older than the Mongol types, older than the Algonquins and most American Indian tribal types. This related beautifully to the deep layers of gravel, glacial drift and silt, one under the other, down to the glacial clay which had held Minnesota Man's body.

These particular layers in the lake area of northwestern Minnesota have given geologists a calendar of Ice Age events, as well as a good idea of what those events were. Around the time Minnesota Man was living in the area, there was an open forest of white spruce, balsam fir, white pine and birch, with scattered bogs of tamarack and black spruce. This forest had recently been destroyed where a finger of the great glacier had thrust southward. The ice overwhelmed the trees, breaking them off and pushing them over into a shallow lake. Then the glacier rolled over the lake, depositing gravel above the buried trees. A layer of peat under the sediment holds the stumps of the trees where they grew. Their logs were cleanly shorn and lay pointing to the southwest, showing the direction of the advancing ice. Such were events in the world of Minnesota Man.

H. M. Wormington, curator of archeology at the Denver Museum of Natural History, pieces together a theory of her story. She was drowned quite suddenly by an accident, such as stumbling into a flash flood in a ravine or being caught by a landslide from the lake's embankment. Her body was held at the bottom of the lake by sediments which piled up over it so that her family never found her. It was preserved under the ice water and when the lake evaporated the hardening sediments held her skeleton intact. She became deeply buried under successive layers of silt and gravel—while some 20,000 years passed over.

This gives us a round-figure estimate for the earliest time human beings inhabited the American forest. It is way back, much deeper in the Ice Age than archeologists had previously thought. It means that a more ancient type of man reached the midland of this continent millennia before the Mongol ancestors of the woodland Indians crossed the Bering land bridge. It means that human eyes, peering between the tree trunks of forests, saw what is to us a very unfamiliar sight—the white cliffs of giant glaciers standing in our United States.

But can an event as great as the arrival of men to take over a whole continent of untouched forest and wilderness be dated by the skeleton of one young girl? Where were her people? Why were not other skeletons found with big teeth, protruding jaw and a long skull? What other evidence do we have of those archaic people?

Although 20 thousand years ago the trees of our land were the same kinds that grow in America today, if you had ventured into those forests you would have encountered many incongruous beasts—some nightmarish like the smilodon (saber-toothed tiger), the dire wolf, the bulky heavily armored ground sloth, birds with 12-foot wingspreads; some awesome like the emperor mammoth; others oddly in the wrong continent like the camels, wild horses and storks. When the last Ice Age, known as the Wisconsin Glaciation, was at its height the forests all across the continent south of the glaciers teemed with these animals. Florida was overcrowded with them at that time. It has been likened to a zoo of fantastic monsters.

What caused all these animals to vanish utterly about 20 thousand years ago is one of the great mysteries of the American wilderness. They may have perished when spreading glaciers of the Ice Age pushed them together until the beasts killed each other off, or died of overcrowding. (Large animals require a certain size of territory to hunt in.) Or disease may have killed them off, when animals of cold, ice-strewn lands, became herded together in warm, humid places farther south. The interesting fact is that some of them were still around when men first came into the American forest and hunted them with spears before bows and arrows were invented.

In a lonely corner of our country north of Fort Collins, Colorado, near the Wyoming line is an area at the top of the high plains in the rain shadow of the Rocky Mountains where few drops of rain water ever splash on the glaring, sun-baked ground. At rare intervals a cloudburst high up in the mountain valleys sends a flash flood down the arroyos, chiseling them into canyons. In 1934 a man with a zeal for rocks and fossils was making his way along a ledge of one of the loneliest of these silent arid canyons when he caught sight of a black horizontal stripe of earth seventeen feet below the rim. This casual discovery led to the unfoldir of one of the most dramatic stories of primeval people in our forests.

Oddly, no human bones were ever found at that site, but four years of excavating by scientific teams brought to light the clear details of events which took place there 20 thousand years ago. At that time it was a well-watered area—springs, bogs and forests and an abundance of wild life. Apparently it was headquarters for an archaic people who came from far and near to meet in convention once a year at the height of the hunting season. They traded with each other treasures of shells from the Gulf of Mexico, volcanic rocks from the Yellowstone region, flint spear points, knives made of elk's antlers, awls of bison's horns, meat scrapers, hammerstones, rubbing stones, and tubular beads strung on thongs. Such were the artifacts of Stone Age people who were leading abundant lives in the American wilderness many thousands of years before the bow-and-arrow and pottery Indians came.

Several thousand of these articles were discovered piled up in one place. These ancient peoples had evidently enjoyed excellent hunting in the area, and had brought together, roasted and eaten animals which no longer exist. One pile of bones was the remains of a banquet in which more than nine big-horn bison were devoured. On the menu were also camels and mammoths. Considering that no cold-storage facilities existed and only two-legged transportation was available for bringing the carcasses to the banquet, the wilderness in that area must have literally teemed with beasts that are now extinct. Even more incredible is the silent, eloquent evidence of spear points in the skulls and ribs, telling us that the people brought down the beasts with hand-thrown javelins tipped with mere 2-inch, chipped-stone spearheads. No human bones were found. Thus we assume it to have been the site of friendly banquets of people who came from far and wide, and who scattered and went their ways after the superb steaks were eaten.

In that same region, 20 thousand years later, men gathered again for trading and feasting. The famous Annual Rendezvous of the Mountain Men reached heights of revelry in southwestern Wyoming in the 1820's. St. Louis had become the booming outpost of the fur companies when Mountain Man, Jedediah Smith, discovered South Pass over the continental divide in southern Wyoming and descended into the Green River

Valley. Here was the richest beaver country that the eyes of mountain men had ever beheld. In this secret corner of the wilderness millions of valuable furs were growing around the ponds and along the streams. The only trouble was that over a thousand miles of pitiless plains had to be crossed twice by men coming to the Green River Valley to pick up the wealth and carry it back to the market in St. Louis.

William Ashley, who thought in big terms, hit on a big idea. He organized pack trains that stretched across two horizons, brought supplies over the plains and established a fur-trading market on the banks of the Green River. Announcement of a Great Rendezvous to be held at that spot was made a year in advance and broadcast by the word-of-mouth network to the remotest camp fires of Indians and mountain men. On July 1, 1825, they converged on the area "from all over the west." The caravans which had brought out the rendezvous supplies flowed back to St. Louis loaded with furs. For ten years after that, people gathered from all over the West for the Great Annual Rendezvous held near South Pass. But the piles of bones they left were bison, elk, coyote, grizzly bear and beaver, not camel, mastodon, smilodon and ground sloth.

How long did the forests of this continent wait for people to live in them? The question is of course anthropocentric. It implies that the forest was of no value until it supplied wood, furs and food for man. But the arrival of the forest is not at all related to the arrival of the human race. To calculate the origins of forest trees familiar to us, we must abandon the human calendar and plunge into the dizzy abyss of infinity.

Astonished geologists found rocks in Arundel County, Maryland, with fossils of a forest that was growing there 75 million years ago. It had peculiar features; it was not like our forest. It was a forest crossing a threshold from the Age of Reptiles to the Age of Flowering Plants. That Maryland forest had about a hundred species of trees. Of these, three quarters were cycads, ginkgos, fern trees and extinct types of conifers. One quarter of the species were "new-fangled" trees which could swing with the seasons, drop their leaves in winter, and burst out in the spring with fresh new twigs, leaves and flowers.

Five million years later (a mere 70 million years ago) the then new-fangled, but to us familiar, kinds of trees began to dominate the area from Martha's Vineyard to the Potomac River. The forest in New Jersey, for example, now contained two hundred species, mostly new style. Cycads, ginkgos and fern trees were rare. The pines, with some fifty species, flourished on sandy soils. Here was a mixed forest of pines and summer-green, leaf-dropping trees—70 million years ago—resembling New Jersey's pine and leaf-dropping tree forests of today!

Dr. Frank H. Knowlton, formerly geologist of the United States Geological Survey, in referring to that phantom forest says:

> If a student of present-day trees and shrubs could have wandered over the hills and vales of Maryland and Virginia he would have found himself quite at home among the trees and shrubs growing there. He would have recognized with reasonable certainty most of the families represented, and in many cases could have placed the plants in or near living genera, so little have they changed in coming down to the present. No less than sixteen modern families of flowering plants are represented.

What are some of the plants which Dr. Knowlton terms "modern" that were growing in that Maryland forest 70 million years ago? They were willow, poplar, beech, elm, mulberry and sassafras. Scrambling up their trunks were three of our best-known vines: grape, climbing bittersweet and Virginia creeper. Water lilies floated in ponds in that forest, opening and closing with the rhythm of the sun as they do today.

When America's first hardwood forest had spread from Virginia to Massachusetts, it contained the tulip tree (erroneously called yellow poplar by lumbermen today, it is a member of the magnolia family), maple and persimmon; there were cattails in the bogs—and "an oaklike tree."

The title of king of the American hardwoods today would go to the white oak. This monarch of our eastern forest supplied the strongest ship timbers, the most time-defying flooring, panels and furniture of the pioneers. Only oaks produce acorns, by which they are unmistakably identified. The rugged, wide-spreading old trees growing solitary in our fields where they were left to shelter livestock are usually oaks.

It is an oaklike tree growing in the ancient Maryland forest which we particularly hail. The other trees round about had developed a number of species indicating that they had been evolving for an unknown length of time, but the oaklike tree was not a specific kind. It was a generalized oak tree; it represents an archetypal oak tree. For this reason, it is considered to be the starting point of the royal line of oaks that are the pride of our American hardwood forests.

If we consider that oaklike tree as a cornerstone, it establishes a date on the geologic calendar for the coming of age of the summer-green forest that spread from the Atlantic Coast to the Mississippi Valley.

By subtracting from 70 million the 20 thousand years since early Stone Age people were hunting prehistoric animals where white cliffs of ice glittered on the northern horizons, we know that the forest waited 69,980,000 years for people to come to live in it.

This is the awe-inspiring time dimension of the American forest. Through time beyond human intellect to comprehend, our oaks, elms and maples, with their company of shrubs and vines, were scattering their seeds, thrusting up their trunks, flaunting their flowers and creating a lively, beautiful blanket of wildness. That was how long they were the dominant life on this continent—with no relation at all to human life.

chapter two

Discovery

THEY were an odd sight, forty bewildered men huddled together on a beach, staring at a forest. They wore the trappings of men who might have just stepped across the drawbridge of a medieval castle instead of out of a rowboat. Polished breastplates and helmets sparkled in the sunlight and banners waved in the breeze. They grasped drawn swords and stared about warily, as though expecting at every instant to be set upon by an enemy. Yet even in that atmosphere of apprehension these soldiers of fortune were pervaded by a profound sense of relief and gladness feeling the ground under their feet on a fine sunny day in 1492 after being cramped in a cavorting little caravel for seventy-one days.

When Columbus got back to his cabin that evening, he made a note in his diary. It is the first historical record of Europeans seeing the American forests. It was a dark forest of tall, straight trees "stretching to the stars with leaves never shed" that stood like a curtain of mystery at the head of the beach.

When the Spaniards stepped ashore the white ribbon of sand between the blue water and the black forest was empty as far as the eye could see. Only the motion of tree tops quivering in the gentle breeze of a fair day, and the waves sliding back and forth on the sand broke the stillness. The men too were silent in utter bewilderment, and they tried to muffle the

11

clank of their swords and shields. Then one grunted in low tones, plucked the sleeve of his neighbor and pointed to faces in the shadows peering out from among the tree trunks. "By midmorning a few came forth from the shadows" and stood in full view for a better look at the gods who had come gliding over the horizon on white wings.

The dark forest of tall straight trunks from which Indians stared at the men in armor consisted of stately slash pines which crowded the Bahamas and the Florida mainland at that time. But the forest was un-welcome, for it blinded the mariners' eyes and it teemed with savages. The southern part of Florida around the bend on the Gulf side was even more repellent with a ghost forest of mangrove trees. The little trees up to 40 feet high grow atop baskets of crooked roots by which they are held above the water, but below the surface the interlocked roots of the man-grove forest entangle oars and threaten the legs of men stepping out of landing boats. Hazards were increased by poisonous snakes and there were rumors of machineel trees secluded among the mangroves. It was said that rain dripping from their leaves, would raise cruel blisters if it touched the skin and that to eat its fruit meant sure and agonizing death.

So it came about that the first colonies on this side of the Atlantic were on the islands of the Caribbean and on the coast of Mexico where forests do not front the sea. The Spanish colonists transported horses across the ocean for fighting infidels and plundering their cities. They shunned forests. They sought the kind of country where the horses could be used, the kind of land they knew in treeless Spain.

English and French explorers arriving on the northeastern coast were confronted by tall, straight, white spruces whose roots could take hold where granite vibrated from pounding surf and whose needle-leaves pros-pered in salt spray and cold sea fogs. Southwestward from the granite coast the sand dunes of what today we call Cape Cod, Long Island, New Jersey and Virginia were crowned by low, tough, wind-loving pitch pines. Below Cape Hatteras the continental coastline dissolved into a complex of shifting sands, shoals, inlets and swamps where on drier acres nature left impenetrable tropical-like tangles of vines, holly, live-oak, magnolia, loblolly pine and bald cypress.

To men viewing this interminable wall of forest from their ships, the inlets and gaps with sand dunes would be conspicuous and welcome—the windswept high dunes on Cape Cod, the broad opening of the Chesapeake Bay and the white offshore sand bars in the Cape Hatteras area. It is no coincidence that these openings in the coast forest became the sites of the first English colonies at Roanoke Island, Jamestown and Plymouth. The English were no more forest-minded than the Spaniards.

The Pilgrims at Plymouth were promptly involved with the forest and the woodland Indians. However, this was not to their liking. They landed first on the tip of Cape Cod where, failing to find water, they were forced to cross the bay to the wooded shore. As Thoreau points out in his book *Cape Cod,* the Pilgrims had few pioneer qualities. "They did not go at once into the woods with their axes. They were a family and a church, and were more anxious to keep together, though it were on the sand, than to explore and colonize a New World."

For a whole century after Columbus the American forest-wilderness was untouched primeval splendor, its vast length and breadth unknown, unexplored, out of bounds to settlers. It held an elemental power by which it fended off all comers from Europe.

When the European discoverers found the American forests teeming with savages, they assumed that those naked red-skinned people had always been there. Then as man's curiosity increased with his knowledge and he was confronted by evidence of the origin of man in the Old World, he invented all sorts of tales to explain the presence of people in a hitherto undiscovered continent. There were legends about the vanished continents of Mu and Atlantis which had provided stepping stones between the two hemispheres. The possibility that primitive man made trans-Pacific voyages on rafts was also suggested. But if such a highly improbable event occurred, the raft party which survived the perils of helplessly drifting for many weeks on the wide and stormy Pacific, would have come much later and could have played no part in peopling the North American forests with Mongol types from northeastern Asia. The primitive Mongols were hunters; they built no boats.

Modern science explains man's first discovery of this continent by a dramatic geologic event. We know that the Aleutian Islands are a chain of volcanoes marking an immense crack in the earth's crust which rims the continental mass from Alaska down the coast of Asia via the Japanese Islands, the Philippines, all the way to Borneo. North of the Aleutians the continental mass is intact. *America and Siberia are joined.* The Bering Sea and Bering Strait are a valley which happens to be flooded with sea water at this time.

Soundings around the west coast of the Alaskan Peninsula show how shallow the water is. It is so shallow that when the last Ice Age was at its height, the glaciers locked up so much water that Bering Valley was dry land. Until about 10 thousand years ago, *it was a simple matter to walk from Siberia to Alaska on foot.* Then water from the melting glaciers of the fading Ice Age caused the sea level to rise 300 feet. Prior to that, the land connection between Asia and America would have been as much as a thousand miles wide.

Eskimos and Indians are recognized as Mongol types by their high cheek bones and other facial features and by the shape of their skulls. The camping places of primitive men have been found on both sides of the Bering Strait and the flint spear points and tools and other artifacts show that these camps in the two continents were occupied by tribes with identical customs and artifacts.

Yet how could the ancestors of our woodland Indians have crossed into Alaska when the last Ice Age was at its height? Was not that whole area buried under ice? Modern geology says no, quite the opposite. The Ice Age did not bury North America under one vast unbroken sheet of ice. The continental glaciers were vast but regional, with one rising in Labrador, another near Hudson's Bay and local glaciers in the western mountains. North of the big ice sheets in Alaska the land was not covered by ice. Spruce forests, berry bushes, game birds and animals, perhaps the Yukon River with salmon, put out a welcome mat for the nomadic hunters who crossed what geologists call "the Bering land bridge."

The picture of the first people who found the American forest is not that of men crowded on rafts or crude boats, but of a family gathered around a camp fire. The upper parts of their bodies are naked, and they wear the fur of bear or musk ox around their waists. The family has a wolflike dog which they have caught in the wilds and tamed. The fresh hide of a newly killed bear is spread out on a boulder to dry in the sun. They feel no excitement of discovery except that one man, holding a spear with a flint point, may give a few grunts which means to the others, "Good hunting here!"

Doubtless when those hunters came upon the forests of this continent by following game trails, they thought the American forests more hospitable than did the shore-clinging colonists who came some 10 thousand years later and found the savages in full possession.

Cabot's landfall was made on the northeastern coast of America in 1497. The English were thoroughgoing mariners, their abode was a ship, their outlook the reaches of the sea. They were not land explorers. And then, the closely packed, deep, dark forests which they saw standing silent and unbroken along the coast were an unfamiliar and fearful sight in English eyes at that time. Vast wilderness abounding in wild beasts and huge birds (such as wild turkeys resembling ugly dragons) were not to be found in England.

If such a wilderness had ever existed in the British Isles it had long since been trampled and destroyed by English, German, Roman and French armies through 1,200 years of successive invasions. Only isolated fragments of England's ancient oak-beech forests were left on estates which were predominantly rolling moor and pastureland and treeless bogs and meadows. The forest groves that still existed had lost all respectability by becoming the hideouts of outlaws and brigands. What was left of the estate forests was about to be "modernized" in accord with the prevailing opinion of forests in Queen Elizabeth's time. When the Queen traveled she sent men ahead to the estates where she planned to stay overnight with orders to create "a most parkly ground, a romancy pleasant place out of what is all horrid and woody."

The history of the second Cabot expedition in 1498 reveals the exploring Englishman's lack of curiosity concerning Indians, trees, or anything that had to do with the American forest. Sebastian Cabot sailed the eastern seaboard from Labrador to Cape Hatteras. This would have carried him past the spectacular forests of birch, maple, larch and fir on the cliffs of Cape Breton in all their late spring finery; across the Gulf of Maine, past Monhegan where great auks would be diving through the surf for fish; past tall red spruces standing on a thousand islands; past the mouth of the Merrimack River, where thousands of gulls and ducks would be following the sediments out to sea; past Cape Cod, Nantucket, Martha's Vineyard and Long Island, where forest clumps of pitch pine would appear like beautiful cushions, bright green at that time of the year; and down the piney coasts of New Jersey, Maryland, Virginia and North Carolina.

The whole coast would have been alive, not only with whales and porpoises wheeling in the ocean, but with one of the greatest bird spectacles of all time—eagles, hawks, wild turkey and heron above the beaches, shearwaters diving and weaving among the waves, gannets diving like white lightning, cormorants standing on floating logs with their wings outstretched, black and white Wilson petrels following in the wake of the ship, northern phalaropes in large flocks rising and wheeling in perfect formation, royal terns and laughing gulls, whistling swans and honking geese. All these signs and sounds of the fabulous wilderness, and perhaps even the fragrance it breathes in June, should have reached off-shore to Sebastian.

Did he and his men land somewhere to eat strawberries and blue-berries, to pick beach plums and enjoy hickory nuts, to build a fire and have roast duck or venison? Not a word about such matters comes from Cabot. The American forest wilderness was just in his way.

To understand such indifference we must forget that feeling of summer cruising in motor boats where cottages dot the shore and a Coast Guard is always ready to bring aid. The people who came across the ocean in Cabot's day were tough soldiers of fortune, their crews, and later the first colonists, were often men who preferred the risks of crossing the ocean sea to suffering in jail or under religious oppression. Arriving on an un-charted coast, crowded in a small sailboat, they were in mortal danger every instant from shoals and reefs. They came and died by the thousands. Their boats were swamped by storms and wrecked. Disease, starvation and thirst dogged them and hundreds were killed by whirring arrows and deadly tomahawks. This is why, for almost a hundred years after Colum-bus sailed, few Englishmen set foot within the American forest-wilderness and lived to tell the tale.*

The prophets of the wilderness who would give us the tradition of splendor of the American forest and its wild life were centuries in the future. Some day would come men like John Bartram, who collected American plants and sent them to England where they became sensations in the gardens of aristocrats; Alexander Wilson and John Audubon, whose paintings glorified the birds of the primeval America in all their colors; Henry David Thoreau, the philosopher who made his cabin in the New England woods famous around the world; John Muir, who led a seventeen-year battle that preserved the sequoias of Yosemite Valley; Theodore Roosevelt, the naturalist President, whose pen created thirty-

---

* Exceptional was the incredible journey of three young English sailors, David Ingram, Richard Twide and Richard Browne, who walked through the forest of the Atlantic seaboard in 1568-69. They were members of a raiding expedition of John Hawkins, one of Queen Elizabeth's buccaneers. Their ship disabled in a battle with the Spaniards, Hawkins put the young sailors ashore on the Gulf of Mexico. They were picked up fifteen months later by a French vessel off Nova Scotia. They kept in touch with the coast and "navigated" by the stars. They were unarmed and made friends with the Indians, who fed them and helped them on their way.

eight national refuges for wildlife; John Burroughs, log-cabin poet-naturalist, who felt the spiritual wealth of trees, wild flowers, birds and small animals, and left this note for us, "The most precious things of life are close at hand, without money and without price."

chapter three

The First Forests

THE summer-green forests of the eastern United States did not appear among the ancient cycads and ginkgos by simply coming up out of the ground in Arundel County, Maryland. Willows, poplars, oaks, sassafrases and other deciduous trees must sprout and grow from seeds of their own kind.

The finest example of this kind of forest is found in the hardness of oak, maple, hickory and walnut; in flaming fall foliage, in the mist of opening spring buds, in pageants of flowering dogwood, cherry and shadblow; in splashes of wild flowers on the forest floor, in abundance of nuts, fruits and berries, and in the play and charm of birds and animals. This describes the forest here in the United States, which is known as the Appalachian forest. Its backbone is the ancient Appalachian Mountain Range that runs from Maine to Georgia; from it, trees flood east to the Atlantic coast and west to the Mississippi. It is identified with hilly rocky country, broad sloping meadows, rushing streams and rich bottom land.

It seems absurd that such a motley forest congregation could have traveled from one hemisphere to another—from Asia to its present location. Yet convincing evidence indicates that this happened, that the Appalachian forest of the eastern United States did, indeed, come from Asia many millions of years ago.

In the 1860's Asa Gray, the impeccable authority on Appalachian plants, astonished the Harvard department of botany by identifying 92 families and 155 genera of trees and flowers as *matched pairs* in northeastern Asia and northeastern United States. This included such distinctive woodland flowers as trailing arbutus, jack-in-the-pulpit, skunk cabbage, trillium, columbine, wild geranium; keynote trees such as chokecherry, witch hazel, sassafras; such vines as climbing bittersweet, wistaria and poison ivy. In a remarkable forest near Darjeeling, India, at around 7 thousand feet altitude, grow hickory, walnut, sycamore and many other familiar trees. Our tulip tree has its only counterpart in central China. The only other species of May-apple is in the Himalayas. Cinnamon and sensitive ferns are paired in eastern Asia and eastern United States.

In 1945, while delving into the geologic history of our forests, I discovered an article in an English scientific journal about a fossil ghost forest which an explorer had found on the foggy icebound west coast of Greenland. It described how a glacial finger of the ice cap had cut a deep canyon through mountains fronting Baffin Bay, and exposed near its bottom, beneath hundreds of feet of volcanic crust, a signal layer of sandstone deposited 100 million years ago that was replete with fossils of parts of trees that were growing in the area when the sandstone formed. There were outlines of seeds, leaves, twigs and even bark markings, identified as those of maple, oak, walnut, persimmon, tulip tree and sycamore. Associated with these were fossil parts of cone-bearing trees—sequoia, juniper, pine and bald cypress. Most puzzling of all were a few fossils from eucalyptus and breadfruit trees which are native today only in Australia and South Pacific islands.

Everything about the ghost forest seemed impossible. Greenland is burdened with an ice cap that domes to two miles deep. How could temperate—even tropical—trees have grown there? By some fanciful chance, a stray seed of sycamore, elm, or walnut might have been carried across oceans by intercontinental birds or winds, but a forest corporation, with bushes, vines and flowers, simply could not have been transported that way.

I was seized by a great desire to see this marvelous sight. But its exact location was a mystery. Apparently none of the writers who referred to "the Greenland Cretaceous flora" had ever personally visited the spot; they only referred to each other's reports.

One day in the Harvard Library I felt a thrill like that of Cortez when he caught sight of the Pacific from a peak in Darien. I held in my hand a crumbling brown pamphlet from one of those never-opened bundles that a faithful librarian had tied up with a red ribbon a long time ago, and I read these words: ". . . on the mainland of Greenland, facing the north shore of Disko at Aternakerdluk . . . !"

I discussed the information contained in the pamphlet with Admiral Donald B. Macmillan, the famous Arctic explorer, who took an immediate and lively interest in the idea of visiting the site of the earliest hardwood forest known to have grown on earth. The dangers and difficulties of reaching the area—navigating uncharted waters, penetrating the polar ice pack, sailing among tremendous icebergs along the west coast of Greenland—presented no insurmountable obstacles to Macmillan. Restlessness of spirit, inborn curiosity, the love of a fine schooner, made Mac ready and able to put ashore a small party of scientists and adventurers at Aternakerdluk for a spooky experience on a July night in 1947.

Everything about the setting was incongruous. The search ashore lasted from 11 P.M. to 5 A.M., but it was daylight the whole time, the dusky, overcast kind of daylight when from a distance shadows are black but close-up objects are clearly visible. Six gentlemen in a dinghy spiked with crowbars and pickaxes—a professor of geology, an ornithologist, a botanist, a law student and two college men—could well have been taken for a band of pirates bent on hiding their loot. The rowboat broke the surface of a cold, gray mirror of water that was sprinkled with white icebergs in surrealist shapes, motionless where they had run aground in shallow water near the shore.

We stepped ashore on a gravel mound formed by the outwash at the base of a tremendous ravine. Each man had his own thoughts about what he might find hidden in the shadowy depths of that fantastic gorge. Ptarmigan, murre nests, eider ducks, blue fox, gold ore? Each of us was awed by the wonderful setting of rock, ice, water and sky in the eerie arctic twilight. The immense dimensions, mysterious shadows, held us in a spell of elemental silence.

What happened during the six hours after the landing is best told by the entry in my diary on the following day. The entry is headed, "Written at Igdlorsuik, July 23."

"It is now 24 hours since we left Aternakerdluk. We were literally pushed out of there by icebergs brought by a gale with snow flurries off the ice cap. Bucking against tough winds from the southeast and with black clouds sending icy rain and sleet splashing on our decks, we threaded our way through the bergs that had clustered around during the night, set our sails, turned off the engine and, like a white bird in a purple storm, we sailed northwest through the Vaigat.

"The brief vision of Aternakerdluk was gone like a dream—its spell and the glimpse which it afforded into the space of timelessness will now always be only a haunting memory. But throughout my life, the events of last night will come to mind again and again, and step by step I shall re-explore the colossal jagged crack in the mountain, and forever see the never-to-be-taken photographs—the purple and white flowers between the water's edge and the cliff, the countless ledges and shelves made by broken slaty projections from the walls of the weird ravine.

"The purple waters of Disko Bay, which had been so free of icebergs when we arrived, became, by a change of wind, suddenly cluttered with icebergs of every size and shape. In the distance loomed the deep sapphire mountains of Disko, topped by the dome of that island's personal ice cap, with massive glaciers winding down to the sea, immobile white rivers. Across this scene, heavily sculptured clouds charged, breaking the mountains and their frozen rivers into huge fantastic fragments—the power of the hurricane blizzards utterly silent in the distance. While the eastern sky was aglow with red and gold and jade, the great power of light brought by a new day seemed to wipe out the Shrine of Aternakerdluk and the unseen ages closed over it again. . . .

"We had arrived in the area in calm weather only eight hours before, and dropped anchor at 11:00 P.M. in about three fathoms of water near a lagoon. The sandy lagoon was unusual. In the granite and basalt kingdom of the north there is little sand, but at this spot the rare outcropping of sandstone had made a dark, sandy beach at the water's edge between tide lines. We unearthed from the bilge a crowbar, sledge hammer and small stone-cracking tools. Six men (Bill, Art, Ed, Dave, A.B., and myself) put over the dinghy. Fifteen minutes after anchoring, we were on the beach and the ravine opened up at our feet, zigzagged above us into the sky.

"This was the inner sanctum, the strong box of the ages where the first hardwood forest that is known to have grown on earth is deposited— here the forms of leaves, seeds, twigs and wood were fixed indestructibly, never coming to light until we dug them out, and were there to see them with our own eyes. The privilege of that moment is beyond measure. The fact of it, the wonder of it, is beyond comprehension.

"We had advanced across the beach only a few steps when we saw stones shaped like huge lemons here and there among the boulders in the outwash from the glaciers up in the sky. The big sandstone lemons alerted Bill, the geologist, who said this was an indication of fossils, and he set to work splitting them open with a hammer. Nothing inside—but wait.

"We climbed over the big mound of the outwash. On either hand among the boulders were vigorous patches of fireweed that extended as far as the eye could see along the base of the cliff. Between the band of boulders with their purple fireweeds and the high water line was a broad bank of gravel, peppered with creamy dryas (arctic roses), white bulbil knotweeds, sedges and mosses, none over two inches high—acres and acres of this flower carpet.

"The ravine swallowed us up and the party quickly scattered, some climbing up to the rim of the ravine to investigate occasional clumps of grass and black crowberry, others with mountain-climbing impulses forging ahead up the steep ravine hoping to reach the ice cap. A.B., the world's most avid stone collector, forged ahead full of vigor and purpose, his nostrils distended by the scent of rocks. In those dusky depths among the infinity of boulders, shoulders and caves, a man could vanish by taking a few steps. So we were no longer a party, each was suddenly alone, the only person in the world. For a few minutes geologist Bill and I were together looking for a stripe of dark shale in the side of the ravine. And then we found it near the bottom, and Bill said he thought this was it, and left me to open it with a pickax while he disappeared higher up looking for another.

"Alone, I swung the sledge and loosened up the rock. It was too loose. Thin layers of brittle slate crumbled and came tumbling out of the wall. Almost every piece pulled out had an impression. One followed another. Here seemed to be the tip and lobes of sassafras, another showed the perfect imprint of part of a sycamore leaf, another perhaps a large fig leaf. Most common were the imprints of elm seeds. I struck a batch of these, where every fragment of shale had an elm seed, or part of one. Frequently little pods appeared, sometimes in clusters. You could even see tiny stalks on them.*

"I clung to that spot and worked alone the rest of the night. Sky,

---

* One of these pods was sent to Dr. E. S. Barghoorn, Paleobotanist of Harvard University, who said that it could be the pod of the redbud leaf tree (*Cercidiphyllum*), a large native tree in Japan today.

clouds, depth of the ravine and these miraculous pages on which was written the astonishing story of a forest of familiar trees which was growing there many millions, millions, of years ago! You can't wrap the mind around that length of time, only around *our* trees. I was overwhelmed and tried to reconstruct the forest in imagination.

"Swinging the sledge, I broke the silence with a crude, cracking blow, and again there was silence as I knelt at the loosened cliff and turned the pages of this cryptic book.

"It was agreed that we would meet at the dinghy at 5 A.M. and row out to the schooner for coffee and breakfast. So I piled up some of the best specimens, planning to return for them later with somebody to help carry them. I was burdened with oilskins, sledge hammer and crowbar.

"Now I was hot—in that gully on an arctic night. I took off oilskins and one sweatshirt, and banged away with the sledge. I looked up at the sky, at the purple mountains across the bay, at the red and yellow in the east, and thought of the big color camera and the photographs I would make of those flowers at the base of the ravine—the clumps of fireweed among the boulders, the white bulbil knotweeds.

"A man detached from the everyday world of common sense gets fanciful ideas. Suddenly the knotweeds were white fingers poked up through the sand by angels who were buried there by the thousands. And then suddenly, as though they had dropped out of the blank grayness overhead, three little laughing gnomes appeared in flesh and blood. We had seen no boat, no hut, no sign of humanity for seventy miles through Disko Bay. The whole area of the ravine and miles in every direction was a vast arctic landscape with no trace of a human being. Yet at that moment (around 2 A.M.) when I was alone, alternately swinging the sledge hammer and kneeling as though worshipping the stones, some slight sound caused me to look up at the lip of the ravine where I saw the three little gnomes.

"They were watching my performance with utter bewilderment. They had probably caught sight of the white schooner from afar, and sped over in their kayaks. Then they had climbed up along the rim of the ravine, following the sound of the sledge blows. And here they found me with nobody anywhere near. Here was a man, madly swinging a sledge hammer at a cliff near the bottom of a gloomy ravine, standing in splashy water in the middle of a raw sleety night. What possible explanation for such behavior could ever suggest itself except that the man *must* be a lunatic.

"They gabbled at each other and then laughed heartily, which broke my reverential spell. I broke into laughter, too, very loud and insane laughter which the far side of the ravine mocked with crazy echoes. I shouted up to them, "Ridiculous, isn't it. . . . What am I doing?" and whatever came into my head. They shouted back, but nobody could understand a word of what anybody said, so it didn't matter. We all laughed the louder. We acted as though we were at a noisy drunken party.

"At the appointed hour, we met on the beach and there found beside our dinghy three little skin kayaks which told how the Eskies had come. They had harpoons and a gun and may have been out hunting walrus when they saw the schooner.

"Before getting into the dinghy and while the others were talking to the Eskies, I ranged over the meadow of dryas and knotweeds and the fireweeds among the boulders. These were the modern successors of the sycamores, walnuts, elms and their wild flower companions in the ancient circumpolar forest which grew there so long ago that even the continents were in different places.

"The wind was high from the east and that was bad; it loosened up the icebergs which had been immobile, and some of them began shoving the schooner.

"The water was now so rough that we had trouble launching the dinghy. When we finally piled in and were on our way there was much splashing and confusion with the oars. The three Eskimos in their tiny kayaks glided alongside, shooting like arrows through the waves and laughing good-naturedly at our clumsiness.

"Back on the schooner, after a cup of coffee, I turned in for an hour's nap, but could not sleep well because I was so excited by the sledging and the night and by the dream of a forest in such a place.

"Suddenly, came dull thuds and jerks as ice collided with the schooner. She was being pushed, despite the anchor, by the bump, bump, bumping against her sides. It was the hour for my watch on deck and the captain ordered continuous soundings. The schooner draws ten feet and we should have twice that depth for safety. Laying the plumb line out on the deck for measuring—we found that it showed less than three fathoms, only 14 feet.

"The storm hit around 5:30 and we tried to hold our position. There were those priceless fossils to get; there were the pictures to take. Then came snow mixed with rain. The weather suddenly thickened and we had to go.

"We sailed away, leaving my pile of shale with leaves, twigs and seeds on the rock up in the ravine, and leaving the flowers and the site forever unrecorded by the camera."

The connection of the Aternakerdluk ghost forest with the primeval summer-green trees in Arundel County, Maryland (and with sugar maples in Vermont, elms in Connecticut and white oaks in Pennsylvania) is no fairy tale. What makes geologic time fascinating—something far other than paralyzing words like Cretaceous or Pliocene—is its magic. When you add more than three zeros to the digits of our pitiful years, anything can happen. The awe-inspiring fact is that geologic events are no more mythical than the Milky Way and much more tangible, for they occurred right here on our planet and left material evidence.

We have no room here for the details of the drama of ice, water and fire, the architects of the American forests and wilderness, wherein Pacific waters teeming with sharks roll across the continent to a western coastline near Pittsburgh, ranges of the Rockies and Appalachians rise and fall and continents drift like crackers in hot soup. But we can trace the origin of the American forests—unless the law of evolution was suspended at some time in the past. In that case, identical miracles of creation would have had to be performed in Asia and North America to summon up the two forests with their filagrees of climbing bittersweets, Virginia creepers, trailing arbutuses, skunk cabbages, Jack-in-the-pulpits, poison ivy, pussy willows and pond lilies.

Begin with Professor Asa Gray's bombshell: that the New England forest duplicates trees in eastern Asia. When a radical theory comes along it is disputed vigorously and Professor Gray's notion was no exception. Ever since the first English colonists came to the New England shores it was well known that the American forest trees were different from the trees of Europe and the British Isles. England has beeches, oaks and elms, but they are of different species. Our white oak, hickory, walnut, our dogwood, wild cherry and crabapple, our witch hazel, sassafras, sweet birch, arrowwood and kinnikinnick, wintergreen and cranberry, are as American as baseball. As for Asia—everything there was considered queer and Oriental. But who could dispute Asa Gray, the honored authority?

It was a time when the natural sciences and exploration was at a high pitch of excitement. In that same year, Darwin announced his theory of organic evolution. Agassiz had just made the sensational discovery that

Dam construction at Gilboa, Catskill Mountains, New York, unearthed fossil stumps of forest 350 million years old. Oldest forest known to have grown on earth.

Ice Age glaciers still burden the land in the far north, and meadows preparing the land for future forests still follow in their wake.

Starved Rock, Illinois, records awe-inspiring past through which forests have marched over the ages. Its quartz was sand on a sea beach when water of the Pacific Ocean covered the area.

glaciers of the Ice Age had recently covered New England, and Commodore Perry had been sent to carry the American flag around the world on the battleship *Mississippi*.

Japan had been a medieval empire, locked up in its islands, closed to foreign influence until 1853 when Perry steamed into Tokyo Harbor, dropped anchor, and sent a friendly note to the Emperor. Few Americans had set foot in Japan before that year. What interests us here is that one of Perry's officers, an amateur botanist, took the opportunity to go off into the hills and collect leaves, twigs and wild flowers which he brought back to Asa Gray. At about the same time, the great plant collector, Robert Fortune, had been commissioned by the United States Department of Agriculture to collect Chinese plants. He made repeated trips to the Orient, including Japan after it had been pried open by Perry.

We can imagine Asa Gray's excitement when plants from China and Japan arrived in Cambridge, Massachusetts, and were laid out on the laboratory table and paired with specimens from the New England woods. At that time, Louis Agassiz was a friend of Asa Gray's in the Department of Natural History at Harvard. Perhaps one day when Louis was passing the door of the laboratory, Asa called out to him to come in and have a look. When the professors bent over the paired species, they agreed that they were alike—but there was a dilemma. It was obviously impossible for a summer-green forest with its bushes and wild flowers to travel from Asia to the east coast of America. It would at least have made a little more sense if our eastern hardwood forest stood on the *west* coast facing Asia.

The controversy that ensued is one of the strangest in the history of the natural sciences. Gray realized that Agassiz's glaciers provided the answer. The New England forest, nudged by the advancing ice, had arrived in New England from the Arctic which it had reached from Asia in an ancient era before the Ice Age. Today we know that this is what happened, but at that time it was a fantastic hypothesis.

Agassiz, who was deeply religious, scored such absurdity. He was a genius when it came to fossil bones. He could interpret the movement of vanished glaciers by sediments and boulders. But for him living things were works of the Creator. The scholarly Agassiz believed that the same kinds of trees arose in New England and in Asia by identical miracles on opposite sides of the Pacific Ocean. Gray could never get Agassiz to change his mind on this point. When Agassiz died fifteen years later he held the same belief.

Asa Gray was right about the part played by the Ice Age in preparing the land and delivering the hardwood forest to the northeastern corner of the United States. This was the last stage of a fabulous journey. But the problem still remained. How does a whole forest cross an ocean? How could a summer-green forest grow in the Arctic?

The theory that the continents were joined together in an ancient age and that they have since broken apart and are drifting around was first stated by Sir Francis Bacon 350 years ago. This may have sounded less absurd in his day than in ours. People who were awakening from the stupor of the Dark Ages found nature bewildering and fantastic, and science was tainted with superstition.

But Bacon's drifting continents received scant notice in the face of such dazzling discoveries as electricity and magnetism, the circulation of the blood and the invention of the telescope. Drifting continents were forgotten for 300 years, until 1915 when a German geologist, Alfred Wegener, pointed to telling evidence that the continents and big islands are fragments of a single land mass that broke up. Wegener likened the continents to icebergs floating in a sea which in this case consisted of soft hot volcanic rock. Granite, the chief material of continents, is 50 percent oxygen, and it floats high in the heavier black volcanic rock that composes the earth's underlying crust.

Wegener's stature as a scientist and the weight of evidence he assembled made it hard to brush off his drifting continents as mere science fiction. But drifting continents are a revolutionary doctrine in our time, and, if it is true that continents are sliding around, much that is said in standard geology texts is erroneous.

But the drifting continent theory could not be suppressed. Evidence for it kept piling up. More and more plants, and many animals as well, were found to be counterparts on opposite sides of oceans. Geologists admitted that mountain ranges with the same rock structure and the same geologic age could be matched on coasts that face each other. For instance, the coal seams of the Allegheny Mountains continue to Nova Scotia where they suddenly break off to reappear across deep ocean water in Greenland. In Greenland they are fractured again under the north Atlantic to reappear in Iceland, Ireland and Scotland.

Dr. Ronald Good of the British Museum, London, devoted a lifetime of study to the mystery of drifting continents. In his book *The Geography of the Flowering Plants* (Longmans, Green & Co., 1947) a classic in its field, he says, "The opinion of plant geographers is almost unanimous that the present distribution of plants cannot be explained without assuming that the now-severed continents have been joined to one another at some time in the past."

Yet for 45 years after Wegener, conservative American geologists and geographers succeeded in bringing drifting continents to a standstill with what seemed to be an unanswerable argument. They asserted that the volcanic rock of the earth's crust, in which the continents are embedded, is so hard and unyielding that there is no force known that could push the continents through it.

On the other hand, opponents argued that the centrifugal force of the spinning earth was sufficient to inch the granite continents along. But this horizontal drag is only 170 pounds to the square foot at the equator where it is the strongest. This strength of pull on a block of granite the size of Manhattan Island (not to mention continents) would approximate the power of 5 thousand large ocean liners hitched to Battery Park, with their engine bells calling for full speed ahead. Manhattan Island could not be towed out to sea by this method. It would not budge an inch.

So the battle of drifting continents was a draw. By 1940, snubbed by American geologists and physical geographers, the drifting continent theory was labeled crackpot and filed away—despite endorsement by European geologists, despite the way animal and plant species appeared across oceans, despite mountain ranges like severed cables and continental outlines that fit together like the pieces of a jigsaw puzzle.

Forty-five years after Wegener, when his name could hardly be recalled and his drifting continents were all but forgotten, a peculiar new kind of evidence turned up indicating continents drifting apart in recent geologic times. Modern computers say that North America is still on a westward course in respect to Europe, and that the Atlantic Ocean is about an inch and a half wider this year than it was last year.

A period of eighteen months, beginning July 1, 1957, was designated the International Geophysical Year. In that period, ten thousand scientists of sixty-six nations cooperated to learn more about the nature of the earth and its surroundings. Data from simultaneous observations in the far corners of the earth were correlated and analyzed. The study of the data will take years to complete. However, first reports, in 1960, referred to a new discovery called "fossil magnetism" as evidence in support of the drifting continents theory.

It seems odd that the earth's magnetism, consisting of invisible electric currents, can become a fossil preserved in the rocks of the earth's crust through the ages. It happens this way. Iron is the metal most easily magnetized and its compound, iron oxide, is abundant in lava. Also, crystallized specks of iron oxide are scattered in sandstone and other rocks. All rock materials when first laid down are either fluid lava poured out of a volcano that spreads over the land, or watery sediments on the bottom of a lake or stream. In either state, before their rock hardens, microscopic crystal needles of iron oxide are free to rotate like compass needles, pointing to the magnetic poles. When hardened in rock, they remain forever pointing in the direction of the magnetic pole as it was when the rock was formed.

When the directions of the fossil magnetic needles from rocks of the same age around the world were compared, it seemed that the North Magnetic Pole had migrated over to Kamchatka in Siberia, to Japan, to our Southwest, and so on at various times in the past. But this is impossible. The spinning earth is a good gyroscope, so that in its path around the sun its axis must eternally hold the angle at which it was tipped after being hurled into space. Thus magnetic poles, which are bound to the ends of the earth's axis, cannot go traveling thousands of miles over the face of the earth. It is the continents that do the traveling!

When, millions of years ago, continents of the Northern Hemisphere clung closer together, ocean currents were different, so climates were different. The Arctic Ocean could have been blue water and Greenland could have enjoyed a climate like that of New England today. This was long before the Ice Ages. It was the time when the forest at Aternaker-dluk was flourishing.

We do not know how that forest came to be in northeast India. Probably it evolved in response to cold snowy winters and warm summers, near Darjeeling. From the eastern Himalayas it must have spread northward when the climates changed. Such a forest could not go southward into the tropics. Northward also lay the widest land for the forest to spread across—the globe of the world shows that most of the land is in the Northern Hemisphere. Accordingly, the hardwood forest spread northward until it circled the lands that were close together there and formed a circumpolar forest.

About 55 million years ago the Cenozoic (Recent Life) Era began, and slowly changing positions of land masses blocked the ocean currents flowing up from southern seas into the Arctic. The Ice Ages came. The forests which had been growing around the Arctic Sea were pushed southward by the increasing cold into all the continents.

At that time Europe had the same kind of trees as North America. But the hardwood forest which was pushed southward in Europe was squeezed against the Alps and the Caucasus Mountains, whose ranges run east and west. And when they could not surmount these mountains, the original species (like ours) of beech, oak, elm and other deciduous trees were destroyed. New species of these trees evolved in Europe after the Ice Age.

In North America it was a different story. High mountains blocked the western part of the continent at that time, but the eastern side offered a wide route southward across land that is part of Greenland today, southward through Nova Scotia, eastern Canada and into northeastern United States. There the older forest, which had evolved in India and China in a former age, found the climate and the land to its liking. This forest spread quickly and easily along the coastal plain of our Atlantic shore, and its regiments marched down the valleys between the Appalachian Ranges.

This then is a brief biography of America's hardwood forest—the gayest, most colorful, most livable and bountiful forest in the world.

But what of our other forests? What about the northern spruces, the southern pines, the northwestern Douglas firs, the bald cypresses, the ponderous sequoias?

These are all members of the great pine family, variously called softwoods, conifers, and evergreens. They are relics which have survived from the age of pines, that flourished millions of years before oaks and elms, grass and wild flowers had appeared on earth. The conifers emerged from the mists of ages, so ancient that it is not possible to theorize about them as we do about the traveling forests and the drifting continents. But North America may have been a cradle of conifer forests, because more genera of these ancient cone-bearing trees are found on our Pacific coast than anywhere else in the world.

The members of the pine family should be viewed with admiration. They formed the first true dry-land forests on earth. The obsolete spore trees that preceded them (tree ferns, club moss and horsetails of the Coal Age) made swamp forests in their time. The dry land consisted of sand, clay, pumice, scoria, lava, granite and blood-red mesas and canyons— scorched by sun, gouged by flash floods, scoured by glaciers. In other words, the continent was a metallic desert, too hot, too cold, too hard, and too dry to sustain trees. The body of the continent was out of bounds for all living things until the pines came along.

Somewhere in dry coves near the swamps, somewhere in valleys where sand was washed and held moisture, the conifer style of tree evolved roots, wood, bark, wind-blown pollen, seeds and cones—everything it took to cope with unfertile land and cold drying winds. Their equipment was to enable the pine family to live in comparatively poor stony soil and invade high valleys, plains and mountain sides, and fling their forests across the continent.

The success of the pine family in occupying ground where other trees falter can be seen in America today. Firs, spruces and larches grow farthest north. Pines are trees of the rockiest heights and of the snow line, of the dryest, sandiest places.

The earliest forest known to have grown on earth, so far as the rock vaults have divulged, was in the Valley of Schoharie Creek in the Catskill Mountains, about 50 miles southwest of Albany, N.Y. Its tree stumps reappeared in 1869 after 330 million years of interment.

Heavy rainstorms bringing flash floods in the late fall were nothing unusual in the experience of the farmers of Gilboa. With crops in, they had only to snatch pumpkins out of the field, check the livestock, and sit it out sleeping and eating around the potbellied stove. In October 1869, a cloudburst hit the Gilboa area, the like of which could not be recalled by the oldest inhabitant. The storm dumped water on the mountainsides faster than the leaf-mold of the forest floor could imbibe it. During the night Schoharie Creek rose, flooded the fields, wiped out the dirt road and carried away the bridge.

Next morning, the storm over, people shrugged their shoulders and set about repairing the damage. Suddenly somebody caught sight of large tree stumps on a stony ledge across the creek. Only the day before that hillside ledge had been covered with scrubby bushes—nothing more. From a little distance it appeared that timber trees had just been cut down, leaving their stumps. But surely this was more a fairy tale than the story of Rip Van Winkle! Even more surprising, when boys climbed up for a look, they brought back the news that those were not real stumps, they were solid rocks that only looked like tree stumps. The village folk had something to talk about.

News of the curiosity leaked out when farmers drove their wagons to market in Albany and gossiped about the rock trees in their town. Eventually, word of the Gilboa tree stumps reached Sir William Dawson, president of McGill College in Montreal, North America's most eminent paleobotanist. But somehow Sir William failed to realize the significance of the discovery. The Gilboa stumps were brushed off as just some old fossils.

A few years later the phantom stumps vanished under another landslide as suddenly as they had appeared, and all that was left of them were a few tall tales and some forgotten notations in an old file up in Montreal. Then, in 1920, bulldozers began tearing down hillsides in that area to build a dam across Schoharie Creek for a reservoir for New York City's water supply.

Its construction doomed the village of Gilboa but caused the miraculous stone stumps to reappear. There were now hundreds of them scattered for a mile along the valley where the mountain sides were excavated. All the trees had been sheared off at about the same height, which told scientists that the forest had been destroyed all at once by a sudden calamity. The trunks had bulbous bases and they were encased in slate, showing that they had been growing in mud. Nearby sandstone indicated that the forest was close to a seacoast—30 million years *before* the old Coal Age forests, which had been considered the most ancient forests of large trees on earth.

Stone imprints of twigs, leaves and seeds were unearthed around their trunks, and these told of a forest of fern trees, the larger ones about 40 feet tall, with trunks 4 feet in diameter. They had light feathery foliage, spraying out from the tops of heavy trunks, and they resembled the fern trees in New Zealand today. The mysterious trees were named *Eospermatopteris,* Greek for dawn-seed-fern.

These trees grew in an age before roots, as we know them, had evolved. The Gilboa trees held themselves upright with heavy straps about 9 feet long which radiated from the base out into the mud and acted as holdfasts. They flexed with the motion of the mud. The solid stone trunks show no traces of wood rings and were probably pithy like palm trees. They were covered with a matting of tough fibers ridged with a good imitation of bark. These were fern trees that reproduced, as ferns do, with naked spores, but they also bore tiny lumps that may have been primitive seeds. If so, here is an exhibit of fern trees experimenting with seeds in an age when real seeds that would revolutionize life on earth had not yet evolved.

What would it have been like to walk in the world's first forest? Probably we, who enjoy the liveliness of a forest, with its colorful flowers, and birds and its sweet earthy scent, would have felt a depressing sense of desolation, as though we were walking in a forest after a fire. There would have been no dense shade cast by the high feathery foliage, no gay mottling of light green and shadowy patches. The sense of emptiness would have been increased by heavy humidity where only the drifting mist was moving among the trees.

There would have been no ground cover of club mosses, partridge berry, or wintergreen; no bush, no herb, no blade of grass. The silence would not have been broken by the hum of insects, splash of frogs, twitter of birds, scramble of squirrels on bark, or the crackling of twigs as a deer leaped.

However, the floor of the strange forest would not have been utterly empty of life—nightmarish giant centipedes and scorpions would have slunk out of the slough and scuttled along mossy fallen tree trunks and the dryer patches of mud. Horseshoe crabs would have been familiar creatures in that forest. After plowing through underwater mud, a huge female horseshoe crab would have staggered out to find a sun-warmed spot to lay her clutch of eggs.

By some weird fluke of fate, horseshoe crabs became a fixed point of evolution. While their beaches came and went during millions of years of shifting lands and seas, generations of this ridiculous animal pursued the ways of their ancestors. We see horseshoe crabs today not much changed from those that inhabited the world's first forest, along bays and beaches of the Atlantic shore, on Cape Cod, in Great South Bay at Fire Island, and among dunes around Cape Hatteras. The horseshoe crab will always remind me of a boy caught without his clothes, trying to sneak away under an upside-down basin.

chapter four

Deciduous Forest

UNTIL recent times, a magnificent forest overlay our country from the Atlantic coast to the Mississippi River, from the spruces of Canada to the cypress swamps of the Gulf coast. We can catch a glimpse of its coattails disappearing around the corner. Our grandfathers beheld it. Descendants of its trees are imprisoned in our parks and reservations. In some places highway engineers and city developers are mobilizing considerable power to blast remnants of woodland. Residual strongholds, particularly in mountains and lake country, can still be found where people yet hunt, fish, breathe forest air and enjoy a personal, first-hand experience of the wonderful forest delivered to them in a kind of modern packaging all tied up with highway ribbons.

Considerable relics of the great deciduous forest remain because of its original immensity, the dynamic nature of trees, flowers and animals, and above all because it was not invaded until recent times. The human population explosion and aggrandizement of cars did not reach obliterating proportions until the last decade.

The forest of the Red Man, the log cabin, Daniel Boone and Audubon has been slain and hewn asunder—but living fragments of the wonderful organism still reflect its original style and grandeur, still impart much of its odors, colors and motions. Our woodlands still perform the age-old

39

celebrations of the revolving seasons with dramatic changes of scenery.

This forest is variously called hardwood, summer-green, tropophytic, cool-temperate. I prefer *deciduous* (from the Latin word "to cut off," "to fall off") because it specifies the outstanding feature of this forest— its leaf-shedding ritual.

The cutting off of leaves and their falling to the ground when winter approaches brings a threefold result of the utmost advantage when nature changes the terms for survival. By halting the flow of sap in a tree trunk, leaf-dropping acts as a gentle anesthetic, putting the tree to sleep for five months each year when its environment may be dry as a desert with water locked up in snowflakes and frozen ground. Second, fallen leaves on the ground are a moisture-holding mulch which turns into brown earth or humus, the richest soil on earth. Third, an arresting fact for people with tired and aging bodies to consider—99 percent of the living structure and organs of a tree is created anew each year. Rudiments (often complete miniatures) of new leaves, which are the food-making organs, and of new flowers, which are the reproductive organs, are packed into buds before the fall leaf-drop. This deciduous tactic restores youthfulness, vitality and freshness annually to the forest—not only in the trees but also in bushes, herbs, birds, insects and animals, all of which are geared to the leaf-dropping cycle of rejuvenation.

I have seen an eloquent example of the survival power of the deciduous plant in polar north Greenland. It is well known that ancient conifers (chiefly spruce, larch, fir)—by dint of the slenderness of their needle leaves, resinous insulation, sluggish growth and rigid form—can resist the drying winds of long and frigid winters. For this reason conifers compose northerly forests near the treeless arctic tundra and the tree-line forests in the bitter winds on high mountains. But a thousand miles north of the conifers, in the land of the polar bear and musk-ox, tiny *deciduous* trees are sprinkled in the polar meadows among Ice Age glaciers.

The trees form scattered mats, not forests; that must wait 10 thousand years. They are willows and birches one or two inches tall, isolated out of the wind in depressions where water puddles and in hollows around boulders. The Arctic night may be nine months long with temperatures 50 and 60 degrees below zero, and the arctic day, twelve weeks of continuous sunlight. During that day these deciduous 2-inch trees fairly explode with life, with the three seasons betokened by opening buds, leaves and flowers in full swing, and leaves turning red and dropping off, all occurring at the same time on the same plant. By this remarkable action each tree builds a place for itself to grow, a soft moisture-holding pillow with its own fallen leaves that coddles its roots through the lethal dry winter where there is no soil.

Those willows and birches, flat on the granite in north Greenland today, could be the survivors of upstanding trees of the forest that grew there before the Ice Age. If so, they used their deciduous skill to survive, howsoever lowly their estate, where all the rest of the forest perished. This supposition is supported by the fact that north Greenland was not glaciated during the last Ice Age. The big ice arose far south of polar America—one center of ice domed up in Labrador, another southwest of Hudson's Bay, from where the glacial lobes headed south. Even today, Greenland, nine tenths covered by a continental ice cap, is ice-free in the north where musk oxen range, blue foxes hunt lemmings and big white arctic hares nibble in the flat patches of the willows and birches. Whether or not the 2-inch willows and birches, isolated in the far north, are waifs from pre-Ice Age forests, they are depending on the deciduous idea to survive in an impossible outpost.

The stage was set on this continent east of the Mississippi River for the world's finest deciduous forest. This is a middle latitude where the seasons are well balanced and without overpowering stress from cold or hot weather. The annual cycles of both temperature and light are broad and gradual. A growing season of six months a year gives time enough to make tall trees with luxuriant foliage, and to scatter pregnant seeds. These conditions created the stately keystone trees—oak, maple, elm, hickory, walnut, chestnut, beech, ash, sycamore, tulip tree, poplar, birch, willow, locust and basswood.

Abundant water through the growing season is another necessity for a superb deciduous forest. One of the most significant features of the eastern part of this continent is the way water is neither localized nor deluged in a brief rainy season, but distributed throughout the year through the length and breadth of the forest. Rainfall depends on winds passing over bodies of water, picking up the moisture evaporated from the surface, and carrying the rain clouds over the land. Where high mountain ranges intercept the clouds (as on our west coast), most of the water is dumped on the windward side leaving areas on the other side arid.

The deciduous forest of the eastern United States can be approached by winds coming over large bodies of water from every direction except due west. Easterly winds pick up water from the Atlantic. South and southwest winds from the Atlantic and the Gulf of Mexico. North and

northwest winds from colder Canada are apt to bring fair weather because chilled air does not condense clouds so readily. But in winter those
north and northwest winds make a generous contribution to the water
supply of our forest by picking up immense snow clouds above Hudson's
Bay and the Great Lakes. These spread the all-important winter snow
blanket over the deciduous forest.

Thus, the region of the American deciduous forest suffers little from
the interception of rain-bearing winds by mountains. The Allegheny
ranges run from northeast to southwest, more or less through the center
of the deciduous forest region, with lush forest to the east and west. The
Alleghenies are older than the western mountains, hence more eroded
by the ages and not so high. Northward they were planed down to half
their former height by the glaciers of the Ice Age. Updrafts of warm air
along the Allegheny Mountains induce clouds to water their well-forested
slopes, but they do not trap all of the rain, because water-bearing clouds
easily glide over low rounded ridges.

Updrafts of warm air from mountainsides tend to form clouds and
increase rainfall. This phenomenon has caused a beautiful lobe of the
eastern deciduous forest to grow on the west side of the Mississippi River
in the Ozark Mountains, where forest trees and woodland wild flowers
resemble those of New England. But north of the Ozarks lies treeless
prairie, and the Mississippi River marks the western edge of the forest.
This would seem strange, since rain clouds should have no trouble crossing a river. It is explained by an eccentricity of the continent.

Directly westward from the Mississippi stretch 2 thousand miles of
prairie and high plains, with no large water surfaces to contribute to rain
clouds. In the Far West, two tremendous mountain ranges stand athwart
rain-bearing clouds off the Pacific. Thus, rains copious enough to support
a deciduous forest can only reach mid-continent from the Gulf. South
winds are funneled northward up the Mississippi Valley and when they
clear the Ozarks they encounter the dry westerlies from the prairies,
which are the dominant winds of this latitude. The rain-bearing winds
northbound from the Gulf are deflected at right angles as soon as they
clear the Ozarks and they head eastward to unload their water across
the great watersheds of the Tennessee and Ohio River valleys. Remains
of the superb forests that formerly filled our midwest can still be seen in
many backwoods hilly areas along the Ohio River and in localities such
as Hocking County, Ohio; Brown County, Indiana, and the area of the
Tennessee Valley Authority.

The American hardwood forest of history—the domain of the woodland Indians, the forest which was so dangerous and unlivable in the eyes of the first English settlers and which we call primeval today—was in truth a luminous, youthful, supple forest, new-born out of the Ice Age. In the nobility and quality of its trees, in the number of species of trees, bushes, vines and flowers; in the purity of lakes and streams, in the abundance and color of its birds and fish and in the personalities of its animals, no other forest that ever grew on earth could be compared with it. Its vitality was revealed in the way it had created trees of various sizes: for stony places and rich bottom land, for shady ravines and sunny hilltops, for south-facing slopes and north-facing slopes. And with the trees were created a host of bushes and herbs by which the forest colonized every niche and corner of its domain.

In a previous chapter we caught glimpses of some of the keynote trees of the hardwood wilderness that grew in North America millions of years before the Ice Age. One of the wonders of the forest is the great age of its sinews, the dateless endurance of its foundations. The millions of years that intervened between those lonely trees of an ancient epoch and the forest of our day left no clue to the fate of the leaf-dropping forest in that long dim period which endured for some 50 million years. Geologists call that time span the Tertiary. The climate appears to have been warmer than today, with equable weather the year round, because fig, lotus and breadfruit—trees of warm climates—spread as far north as Canada in those epochs. The bald cypress of the swamps of our southern states and the sequoias of California, assembled their forests then. But little turns up concerning the sycamores, elms, oaks, maples and the rest of the radiant company of our deciduous forest. Presumably they just lived on and on and on, dodging volcanic eruptions and rising mountains, without fatal challenges from drastic climates.

The grouping and maneuvering of the forest through pre-Ice Age epochs is not important. That the chief trees of the forest in our land are the same *kinds* of trees after 50 million years of challenging adventures in the open air, is awe-inspiring. They survived disruptive events through an infinity of time because they owned the deciduous patent— leaf-dropping, winter buds, all living cells born anew each year, traveling seeds that rolled on the ground or flew on wings, and a peculiar texture of wood wherein the sap flows faster through continuous microscopic tubes.

When the glaciers of the recent Ice Age moved against the veteran deciduous forest, they did not destroy it; they modernized it. The *genera* of the burly trees came through intact, but they pullulated with new species. *Gray's Manual of Plants in Central and Eastern United States* lists thirty species for the beech family (which includes oaks), twenty-six species for the birch family, fifty-two willows, twelve walnuts, nine elms, nine maples and six species of ash.

In contrast, sycamore came through the Ice Age without change—Gray lists but one species. Sycamore is the imperturbable grand old veteran of the American deciduous forest. Its tall boles still line the banks of rivers in the Middle West where they lean over muddy creeks as if they were a little tired. It is one of the few of the original giant trees left after all the slaying of forest during the past hundred years. I have seen a sycamore by the Ohio River near Rabbit Hash, Kentucky, with a bole almost ten feet in diameter.

Look twice at an old sycamore and you will see how it bears the imprint of antiquity. Its bark is smooth, but unlike the smooth bark of the more recent cherries and birches it is inelastic. It rips off as the trunk expands, exposing whitish inner bark. Also the trunk and main limbs of sycamore are heavy in proportion to the twigs—a massive central axis with short slender branches. This is the style of very ancient trees.

The outstanding feature of the modernization of the original all-wood deciduous forest was not the addition of a few new species of conservative hardwoods, but the eruption of little trees, bushes, ferns and wild flowers. The little trees have slender trunks that grow fast and they can bend and reach for sunlight sidewise as well as upward. They went out in front of the tall dark timber; they thronged its sunny borders, mounted cliffs and preempted meadows, swamps and shallow ponds. These were birch, aspen, scrub oak, blue beech, hop hornbeam, witch hazel, sassafras, shadblow, alder, redbud and dogwood.

The rose family staged an extraordinary performance. Under prodding by the Ice Age, it generated a host of little trees, including wild cherry, crab apple, plum, mountain ash and hawthorn. These are native Americans but they are parvenus with no record to connect them with the pre-Ice Age dynasties. In a sense hawthorn might be voted the most modern tree genus of our deciduous forest. It is creating new species before the very eyes of botanists today, faster than they can identify and name them. *Gray's Manual* lists 130 species of hawthorn, but speculates that many of these may be wayward hybrids instead of fixed species that reproduce true to type.

The little trees were summoned into being in sunny places. They did not alter the time-honored quality of dark forest depths where big trunks prevail and the air is still and moist. They added no fine timber—indeed, today's foresters often refer to birch, aspen, alder and scrub oak as weed trees. But the modern little trees certainly brightened the face of the old forest, and they attracted birds and offered good browse to deer and other animals. Moreover, the supple front-line poplars and birches, flaunting white bark and shimmering leaves in the sunlight, lead the hardwood forest onto treeless and infertile uplands, and are the first trees to heal the scars left by windfalls and forest fires.

Our deciduous forest had surprisingly few bushes before the Ice Age. Witch hazel, sassafras, alder and willow probably were yielding both little trees and shrubs, as they are today, but the list of true forest shrubs that are genuine antiques is short. Each antique shrub is like a little tree, or it has some peculiar quality or feature which probably contributed to its timelessness.

The hazelnut bush was making delicious nuts some 10 million years before there were men and squirrels to eat them. It may have been a cross between a hickory and a birch in the ancestral forest. The bush blooms when the snow is still on the ground and its flowers have no petals, but nothing appears in the spring woods more exquisite than hazelnut's tiny flowers made of coral-pink stamens sparkling in the sunlight above the snow.

The holly family, which produces both little trees and bushes in our woodland, was flourishing on this continent 90 million years ago; its members appear in the earliest records of our deciduous forest and there were many more species then than now. Then the hollies disappeared from the record; they went underground, so to speak, and then turned up in our historic forest. In the face of the great antiquity of the holly family, it is a good guess that winterberry, an exciting little holly bush that is common in our woods, was lining its twigs with rich red berries millions of years before the Ice Age.

Where winterberry grows in the cooler parts of the forest spicebush is also found, a fascinating waif from that big clan of southern aristocrats, the laurel family. The delicate flowers of spicebush look like tiny puffs of golden steam in the grey woods of very early spring. But the little tree is best known for the surprise it packs in its twigs. Chew them and you wonder why nature made wood so highly spiced 20 million years before anybody could taste it.

Bayberry encases its seeds so heavily in protective wax that they were used to make candles in colonial New England. And sweetfern, not a fern at all but a twangy little bush that thrives on dry sterile ground, has fernlike leaves with a heavenly aroma. Bayberry and sweetfern are close relatives, sole members of the wax myrtle family with a genealogy that goes back 90 million years.

These American originals have similar personalities. They are prim, aristocratic, conservative bushes or small trees, scattered in the understory where the canopy of tall trees is open wide enough to allow sunlight and rain to reach the ground. They do not clutter the forest floor with brush or form dense thickets and monopolies. They usually like dry places and are thus good companions of the elms and maples, oaks and walnuts. They have interesting and positive survival equipment—seeds protected by hard shell or heavy wax, and twigs and leaves spiced heavily with chemicals which exude a pungent fragrance. Animals and insects do not delight as people do in resinous and oily plant odors. The scent of these bushes were highly effective in fending off browsing beasts that could have chewed them up by the dozen.

The rise of many new bushes in the Ice Age was the most spectacular feature of the modernization of the forest. They transformed the dark and ancient fastness into the lively, varied wilderness which men found on this continent.

Bushes sprang up to fill the aisles and throng the borders of the forest. Where mottled shade and sunlight danced on the forest floor, modern bushes like mountain laurel, arrowwood and moosewood formed an uncrowded understory. Legions of bushes cushioned the forest environment of upland meadows, bogs and shallow ponds.

These were the bushes of the forest that emerged from the Ice Age. They are not to be confused with the malignant tangles and brambles of our man-made age of weeds. Their thickets were compositions in which varieties of bushes were assembled in tune with the sunlight, moisture and fertility of a location.

The diversity of the bushes conjured up between the thrust and retreat of the big glaciers is suggested by their names. Red osier dogwood in bright, lighted thickets from Labrador to West Virginia has rich red twigs that color the grey forest in winter and early spring. Staghorn sumac is well named for its thick twigs, furry like the antlers of a young buck. There are buffaloberry, button-bush, wahoo, kinnikinnick, bladdernut, sweet pepperbush.

New Jersey tea is a dramatic shrub. Its fruits are triangular and explode when ripe, shooting their seeds in three directions. Its name commemorates a time when soldiers of the American Revolution made "tea" with the leaves of this bush after imports from England were cut off. Today this humble shrub is generally unknown and unappreciated in our eastern forest, except by people who enjoy curiosities such as the exploding fruits.

The honeysuckle family put some tall bushes with beautiful light green foliage and brilliant berries into the American deciduous forest—bush honeysuckle, mountain fly honeysuckle, snowberry and wolfberry. (These elegant natives are not to be confused with the alien Japanese honeysuckle that is suffocating our hedgerows today.)

The *Viburnum* genus of the honeysuckle family bestowed on the forest arrowwood, witherod, dockmackie, hobblebush, nannyberry, *quatresaisons des bois,* moosewood, stagbush. These bushes are famous for the quality of their twigs. They are supple, clean-cut, tough and twangy. Their names betoken their popularity among the Indians and early settlers. Their straightness and smoothness made them valuable for arrow shafts, for withes to plait mats and hobble animals, for whips and switches. A blue-black viburnum berry consists of a single stony seed surrounded by a thin bitter pulp—not good eating when fresh, but people who lived off the forest ate them dried, like raisins. Such berries were a special gift to the small birds of the modernized forest—for them the thin pulp was juicy energy, and the seeds, like little pebbles, were just the right size for grit in gizzards.

Now to the royal family of bushes, the heath family, the outstanding bushes of the American deciduous forest from every viewpoint—that of bird, beast and man. Judging by their flowers, with colorful petals and elaborate mechanisms for pollination by modern insects, the heaths evolved in our forest late in the Ice Age, although they are probably descendants of very ancient tropical species.

They touched up the drab old hardwood forest with spotlights of tropical color—rhododendron, rhodora, bog-rosemary, andromeda, mountain laurel (*Kalmia*), and wild azalea. In this category of aesthetic appeal (which, in wild nature, means insect appeal) belong the two smallest bushes of the forest, also members of the heath family, the creeping snowberry or wintergreen and trailing arbutus. One contains the essence of wintergreen in its leaves; the white or pinkish flowers of the other waft a perfume out of all proportion to their size.

The blueberry tribe of the heath family needs no praise beyond the names of its bushes—highbush blueberry, lowbush blueberry, huckle-berry, bilberry, cranberry. These healthy berry-laden bushes, scarcely ever defaced by pests, are radiant and vigorous but never oppressive. They form clean, open thickets, easy to negotiate while gathering hand-fuls of delicious berries. Their foliage is bright green in summer and an arresting scarlet in the fall. These lend the eastern hardwood forest of our country a special quality that appeals strongly to right-thinking people.

The heaths thrive under the influence of warm summer sunlight alter-nating with long cold winters, where air and ground are continually saturated by rain, snow, mist and floods. The greatest stimulants to the evolution of species are metallic ions, such as those produced where minerals in granite are dissolved in water. Thus, new species of the heath family were created that were highly specialized to grow in cold granitic landscapes and bogs. Such conditions were widespread and dynamic in the wake of the retreating ice cliffs—hence, the sturdy heaths.

Before the Ice Age, our northeastern mountains were twice as high as they are now, snow-capped and jagged like the Rockies. The glaciers planed off the White Mountains, the Green Mountains, the Adirondacks and the Laurentians, leaving them much lower, rounded and scarred with outcroppings of granite, with ravines cut by torrents of ice water and cliffs where chunks of rock split off. Today we can see how small and tortured are the trees of rocky highlands—scrub oak and pitch pine. A *montagne* forest is dauntless but impeded, for trees are stunted by bright light and strong winds, and they must be scattered where roots can take hold only in the pockets and crevices of rocks.

In contrast to this are the tall straight trees of lower slopes and valleys where rushing water from glaciers deposited drifts of ground-up granite. It was a glittering domain of boulders, pebbles, sand and clay, holding vast reserves of calcium, magnesium, potassium, iron, sulfur and phos-phorus. As we shall see in a later chapter, these are the metallic elements of sap that spark the growth of trees. Before forests occupied the glacial deltas, these metals were dissolved in the waters of the countless lakes and ponds that filled the undulations of the glacial delta. Yet those waters were still sterile. Metallic elements alone cannot build living things. Roots of trees must have soil in which the metallic ions are mixed with decayed organic matter.

Turning glacial ponds into forest soil was the paramount contribution of the heath family bushes to the modernization of the ancient hardwood forest. Without them, not only would the forest be less colorful and have far fewer birds and small animals, but it would have taken millennia longer for it to spread northward, with tall timber in deep rich soil. The fertile broad-valley farms of the Connecticut, Hudson, Mohawk, Delaware, Susquehanna, Tennessee and Ohio River valleys, Great Lakes areas, and isolated bottomland farms in northern New England and New York State —the sites of the foundation settlements of our people—would not exist. There would have been no states, or cities such as Chicago and Detroit, as we know them. The biography of our continent—and our country— would not read as it does today.

The process of transforming ponds began invisibly when microscopic plants known as *Chlorophyta*—which includes *Volvox,* a swimming plant which, seen through a microscope, resembles a golf ball, and *Desmid,* a Siamese-twin plant decorated with fantastic protuberances and markings —turned up in ponds on the north side of the forest. These amazing microscopic plants multiplied fast and, in a summer or two, their pastures were supporting big populations of bacteria and microscopic animals. The water was thus fertilized with organic life, which spread northward through the ponds and shallow waters along the shores of lakes. Soon masses of this infusoria of plant and animal life floated as scum near the surface where the tiny animals and plants were cooked by sunlight, died, and rained to the bottom. This was the foundation for bog muck.

With the passing years, the bottom muck rose steadily higher and higher under the water. When it approached the surface, the first of larger plants took root in it, and green drifts of sphagnum moss appeared, floating above the muck. The pond, or lake shore, had suddenly become a bog.

Sphagnum moss is the most elaborate and peculiar of the ancient mosses. Its fossils have been found in rocks of the Devonian Period laid down 350 million years ago. It has green cells containing chlorophyll, as ordinary mosses do, but these are buried among large balloon-like cells. These queer cells have thin transparent walls reinforced by spiral bands like barrel hoops which keep them from collapsing. Sphagnum moss, floating on the surface of water, is light grey because the balloon cells become filled with air when they are above the surface. When submerged, water rushes into the balloon cells whose walls are porous. Sphagnum absorbs and holds water like a sponge, keeping a bog wet in the dryest season. When the top layer of moss is air-filled, it insulates the muck underneath, keeping the water in the depths of the moss from evaporating. This makes a sodden, sphagnum bog, a stewpot of fertility to nourish the cranberries of the heath family.

Between the retreating ice cliffs and the advancing tall forest, cranberry bogs covered hundreds of square miles of the glacial delta. They reached from the tundra of Canada deep into our southern states, as far as glacial sediments were spread below the southern face of the ice. The famous black soil of farms in Illinois, Indiana and Ohio, in the heart of the great deciduous forest, is the product of the cranberry bogs that prepared the ground for the forest trees in those areas.

Both sphagnum moss and cranberries make a bog more acid, intensifying the chemical reactions in the water. The muck is a dynamo of vitality when oxygen reaches it by any disturbance of the water, as when something falls in, or wind ruffles the surface. Thus, sphagnum-cranberry bog becomes a magnet for many kinds of marsh plants—swamp willow, cattail, bulrush and cotton grass sedges, water-lilies, arrowhead, and *Menyanthes,* the bogbean. While these plants blanket the bog, floating six feet or more above fluid muck, the bushes of the heath family—blueberry, huckleberry, leatherleaf, Labrador tea—are surrounding the bog and gradually closing in. Hazelnut and buffaloberry are on their heels, and with them come the bushy forms of birch, willow and alder, whose woody roots are tunneling in firm dry land where the bacteria of decay and micro-animals of the soil are at work. A pond is about to disappear, and a threshold between the glacial sediments and the forest is being built on the site. It is almost ready for tall forest trees to step upon it.

Today, even while man is finishing his destruction of the ancient forest, nature's patient operation of converting the ponds and lakes of the glacial sediments into forest land is still going on. Look at a map of the western peninsula of Michigan, northern Wisconsin and Minnesota. Here the northwestern sector of the deciduous forest is peppered with countless lakes and ponds. Sphagnum and cranberry bogs are spread across square miles in a maze of ponds which they have not yet conquered, and of islands and muskeg where aspen and birch, the outriders of the deciduous forest, are mixed with the tough old northern conifers, balsam, white cedar and black spruce.

That so large a sector of the frontier between the deciduous forest, advancing northward, and the realm of the glacial ponds still remains in our day, shows how recently the big ice was here. Indeed, the appalling events which changed the contours of the land and transformed the forest were happening only yesterday afternoon on the geologic calendar. On the northern marches we see before our eyes the final stages of the transformation of that stately old forest into the colorful wilderness of our history.

Twenty thousand years ago ice stood twice as high as the Empire State Building on Manhattan Island. I base this estimate of the height of New York City's ice cliff on the height of a similar ice cliff of a continental ice cap which I saw rising abruptly above fjords in northern Greenland. The glacier on Manhattan marked the farthest advance of the ice on the Atlantic Coast. Long Island and Staten Island are terminal moraines, that is, sediments piled up below the front of the ice cliff. The retreat of the whole ice front (which extended from Manhattan to Cincinnati to St. Louis) is supposed to have begun only 20 thousand years ago.

The rate of retreat varied according to the lay of the land. The evidence of rocks and glacial sediments is that the glacier's cliff took 4,100 years to melt back from Hartford to St. Johnsbury, Vermont—a distance of 190 miles. The gorge cut by Niagara Falls is a telling chronometer. The cutting could not have commenced before the ice barrier in the basin of Lake Ontario gave way, releasing the flow of water at the mouth of the Niagara River. The cutting back of the Niagara gorge is proceeding currently at the rate of about two and a half feet per year. Since the gorge is around seven miles long today, the river has been cutting it for about 7 thousand years.

This tells us how recently the ice left the northern part of the United States. The estimate is also confirmed by the Falls of St. Anthony in the Mississippi River at Minneapolis which have cut back about eight miles since these falls began. This means that the lobe of the big ice left the Minneapolis area 7,800 years ago. Presumably the region of the countless lakes and ponds in northern Minnesota was still under the big ice at that time.

It may seem incredible that the fine deciduous forest of our country was modernized and moved into its site only a little while (on the geologic calendar) before our ancestors came to live here. What would this land have looked like to the colonists if the big ice had not plowed it? The Appalachian Mountains would have been much higher and snow-capped. Valleys, lakes and rivers of northeastern United States and Canada would all be unfamiliar. There would be no Cape Cod, no Martha's Vineyard, no Long Island.

An area of about 10 thousand square miles in southwestern Wisconsin was never iced where the lay of the land caused the lobes of the glacier to flow around it. Here we have a hint of what the deciduous forest might have been like if it had not been modernized. In this area there are no depths of sand, gravel and glacial till. The infertile soil is only an inch or two deep and there is much outcropping rock. The hills, eroded only by water and uncarved by ice, are craggy with vertical sides, which expose layers of very ancient rocks. Old conifers, such as tamarack and spruce, are scattered about, and the deciduous forest is represented by straggling elms, birches and poplars which have their roots in rocky crevices and in bottomland where rain runoff has deposited a few inches of soil. The landscape is sparse and primitive, like a rough sketch of forest land with many details omitted.

What a contrast this is to the luxurious forest that grows on the undulating sediments, where trees are taller, the forest deeper and its borders studded with dark bogs, blue ponds and thickets of bushes laden with berries. The old forest accepted the invitation of the sediments with flying colors—fortunately before the age of weeds.

The close connection between the American deciduous forest and recently vanished glaciers was utterly unguessed until the middle of the last century. That an awe-inspiring forest teeming with birds, fish, and game, could have emerged so recently from under a continental ice cap seemed as preposterous as that it had appeared out of a clap of thunder.

The first news of the fabulous Big Ice came from Professor Agassiz. He told how he was riding on a bumpy, sooty, noisy train between Boston and Springfield, looking out the window at the passing landscape, when he suddenly recognized that this was glacial land. Smooth boulders strewing the ground, gravel in the railroad cuts, polished rock surfaces, reminded him of what he had seen when he was a student in Switzerland, studying glaciers in the Alps.

At about the same time, farmers moving into recently cleared land in southern Ohio and Indiana repeatedly came across something which made no sense at all to canny backwoodsmen. Thirty miles north of Cincinnati, where a creek had cut down through 85 feet of gravel, there was a black layer of earth which turned out to be an ancient peat bog and sticking out of the dirt just above it were logs. Nearby, more logs were found in a gravel quarry 65 feet below the surface of the ground. Farmers drilling wells in southwest Indiana found many logs buried from 60 to 120 feet deep. Elsewhere in Indiana they mined black walnut logs at low water from the base of a creek bank some 60 feet below the floor of the present woodland. These were not fossil wood; they were timber that might have been recently felled. Their wood was preserved from decay by being buried originally in a sphagnum bog.*

Since these Indiana and Ohio trees were the same species as forest trees in the same area today, they must have been overwhelmed in a recent stage of the retreat of the glacier. Their kind could only have been growing there when the main mass of the ice was several hundred miles north. After centuries of fair weather during which those forests matured, they must have been smothered suddenly with rock debris, scraped off the Laurentian shield of Canada and transported many miles south of the solid ice in colossal floods of melting ice water. This could have been a catastrophic rush of water from the collapse of the ice dam that had gripped the Mohawk River Valley and Lake Ontario Basin, when Niagara Falls began 7 thousand years ago.

The trees were buried at different depths where the till was dumped on hilly ground, but the wonder is the great volume of sediment in southern Ohio and Indiana, upon which the deciduous forest of our time, in all its splendor, was growing 50 to 200 feet above its predecessor.

The creative powers of the forest were most active when the ice was in retreat, when successive forest zones were marching northward. The sphagnum-cranberry bogs led the procession. Behind these came a mingled company of birch, aspen and alder with arctic conifers such as tamarack, spruce and fir. Next came the blueberries and their family thickets at the edge of the tall hardwoods. The procession would not have advanced at a constant rate because summer sunlight and winds, now southerly,** fought a running battle with the glaciers. However, the northward advance of the forest averaged fifty miles per century.

The appalling forces released in this forest-glacier epoch left vivid records which tell us that the ice cap, at the time of its greatest spread, covered 5 million square miles of North America and was so heavy that it depressed the bone of the continent. From a study of bluffs overlooking

* The famous PT boats of World War II were made of white cedar logs of a vanished forest unearthed from sphagnum bogs in New Jersey.

** During the height of the ice, areas below the ice face would have had unremitting north winds because air moves from colder to warmer regions. This is seen in the way air pours into a room when you open the window on a cold winter day. But after the ice had retreated a sufficient distance, winds would have started to come through from the south.

the lower Mississippi River, geologists estimate that the Mississippi Valley was pressed down from 300 to 400 feet below its present elevation above sea level.

The Atlantic Coast in the vicinity of Philadelphia, was depressed about 150 feet. The coast of Maine was 200 feet lower, and the depressions were much greater farther north, reaching over 400 feet in the Gulf of St. Lawrence, and around 500 feet in Labrador. Marks made on rocks by the ocean tides in those areas when the ice was at its height show how the land has rebounded (uplifted) by that amount since the glacier vanished.

The mass of frozen water stored in the glaciers was a reservoir of unimaginable power, ready to descend through any available outlet when the millennia of melting came. The assault on the land that ensued left telltales in the sediments piled up from the Atlantic Coast to the Mississippi River.

When the cracking and grinding of rock by the advancing Big Ice ceased, there arose a great mist and a sound of roaring water along a thousand miles of the winding ice cliff. Cataracts many times greater than Niagara poured from the south-facing ice cliff on many levels and rushed out through huge tunnels underneath the glacier. They whirled along with them the rock debris of mountain tops, transporting glacial gravel hundreds of miles.

After this water power had been released by the ice through centuries, the sediments settled down and began to dry. The water grew quieter and ran along freshly formed contours, while lakes and ponds sparkled in the sun. We now see the new forest with the bases of its trees high above the tops of their ancestors.

The city of Cincinnati, Ohio, stands at the edge of the farthest thrust of the ice in that locality. The city is built on a glacial moraine 120 feet above the level of the Ohio River. Yet, this is not the whole story. The bottom of the Ohio River consists of glacial sediment 150 feet deep down to the original rock bed of the river.

The ice-plowed sediments were carried by all the streams that flowed southward from the ice base. The height of the glacial till at the mouth of the Susquehanna is recorded at 245 feet. On the Potomac it is 140 feet; on the Rappahannock, 125, and even on the James River in Virginia glacial till is piled a hundred feet deep.

West of Lake Michigan the sediments were not channeled until they reached the Mississippi; they were spread over hundreds of square miles of prairie-like plain. The depth of even this broad level deposit measures 300 feet at Princeton, Illinois.

The power of the forces released by melting ice is revealed by the way the glacial floods chiseled river valleys. Wherever the rivers received sediments from the melting glacier, they seem absurdly shrunken in the middle of a wide flood plain. For example, the Minnesota River, flowing into the Mississippi from the west, was completely outside the glaciated land. Yet it meanders for 250 miles as an insignificant little stream in a trough one to four miles wide, with an original rock bed a hundred feet below its present bed of glacial sediment.

Below St. Louis the escarpments of the Mississippi Valley face each other across five to ten miles of lowland. Above St. Louis the river valley is between two and eight miles wide. The great river, even though a mile wide in places, seems much too small for its valley. The sides of the original valley are gravel terraces up to 200 feet above the flood plain. They show the high water mark of the last floods of the Ice Age. Such a flood staggers the imagination.

chapter five

The Deciduous Idea

A FOREST throws away its leaves—and lays the foundation for America as we know it.

Have you ever walked in deciduous woodland on that particular week in April when the buds on trees and bushes are bursting, warblers have suddenly appeared, and the confetti of spring flowers sparkles in drifts of sunlight on the forest floor? The spirits rise in response to the surge of life in such a place, at such a time; the senses are in tune with the surroundings, a feeling of buoyancy and bodily well-being ascends and merges with the forest coalition.

Spring is quickly over. The leaves are out and their work of supporting life is in full swing. The birds have laid their eggs, berries are ripening, embryos in seeds and wombs are maturing. In the summer the sun is warm upon the deciduous forest stimulating chemical processes in living cells, quickening their division and building. The shadows of the broadleaf forest beneath fully spread leaves are deep and cool, protecting the young life from the relentless heat of the sun. This combination of sunlight and shadow is a powerful generator. It nurtures a sudden tidal wave of life that must be checked drastically and soon, lest the forest be strangled by its own abundance.

The weather pendulum swings the other way. The drop in temperature slows the chemical processes in living cells, their dividing ceases, growing is almost at a standstill, sap stops flowing in trunks and twigs. Leaves—

57

the food factories of all the great populations of the forest—prepare to flutter to the ground. Insects vanish from the air, dying by myriads, or burrowing under bark and into the ground. Little animals are burrowing, too. Berries and fruits are melting ripe and seeds released from pod and capsule rain to the ground and disappear among the fallen leaves. Many birds head south. Only a few silent hot-blooded birds are left behind to live by prying out insects and their eggs from under tree bark, and to enjoy the forlorn, delicious remains of rotting berries. And a few prowling mammals with built-in furnaces, that can live by eating each other, feeding on hoarded nuts or browsing on bark, are left in the wreck of the forest.

This collapse of the deciduous forest is signaled by a brightness like the flare of a tremendous silent explosion. Foliage suddenly glows with yellow, red and orange as though the forest were aflame. But unlike the green of leaves and the colors of flowers, autumn colors are not directly related to forest life. Each species of tree and bush has its own chemical formula for sap. One kind has more iron than another, or more magnesium, sodium, or phosphorus. Some species of ash, growing in limestone country have an alkaline sap which adds blue to their autumn regalia, giving it a purple tone. Scarlet oak, sweet gum, red maple, sumac and dogwood have slightly acid sap which paints them red. The chemical composition of chlorophyll is such that it reflects green intensely, so when leaf cells are imbued with chlorophyll its green masks the reflections of the various minerals in the sap of different species. But chlorophyll is an unstable chemical; it must have fresh water every instant or it disappears. When sap stops flowing the chlorophyll vanishes and the sap left standing in the leaf just before it falls slowly evaporates, concentrating its mineral solution. The tree flaunts its tribal colors—the colors of leaves about to die.

The poplar, birch, tulip tree and willow are normally bright yellow in the autumn; white oak is tan, beech mahogany, ash and prune purple; red maple, dogwood, sassafras, redbud, sweet gum, blueberry and sumac bushes scarlet, while sugar maple makes the hillsides of New England flame with red and orange.

With its leaves gone, the forest is shockingly different. Trees and bushes are like black skeletons, the wild flowers are shriveled and gone, insects have vanished, and although they had frequently been a nagging nuisance, the absence of their stir and hum leaves a queer emptiness. The forest is almost birdless now; the few birds which remain are slow, subdued and mostly in hiding; the rustle of a lonely squirrel is startling; the creaking of tree limbs somewhere overhead is spooky; the sunlight seems chilly where no leaves reflect it and no flowers or birds respond to it. If a November drizzle or chill mist comes upon the forest, the silent, gray place is utterly dreary.

The leaf-fall of the hardwood forests of the northern Temperate Zone has no counterpart in conifer forests. The evergreen foliage of the conifers changes little the year round, and the highly acid needle-carpet floor of the forest is quite free of herbs and undergrowth at all seasons. Nor is there anything like leaf down-fall in the steaming tropical forests or in the lackadaisical forests of subtropical climates. What happens to the deciduous forest is one of the most dramatic events of life on earth in terms of its sweep and swiftness, and its impact on vast populations of plants and animals. Of course the forest is far from overthrown; but it has been stopped in its tracks with expert efficiency. This happens at precisely the best time. Embryos inside seeds have been formed and packaged with concentrated food on which they can live independently for months, or even years. Living cells that will compose future twigs, leaves and flowers of trees have been segregated and some have already made miniatures of those structures and encased them in buds placed at the right locations. With these arrangements made, and with growing halted, no more food is needed from leaf food factories. Every living part of the tree above the ground has completed arrangements, with incredible resourcefulness, for the downfall of leaves.

The insects imitate going to seed. Adult insects are primarily reproductive organs, like flowers—some of them, such as butterflies, moths and beetles are brightly colored. All flowers of the wild forest, from the purple ones on the highest twigs of elm and the yellow male catkins of oak to the violets and trout lilies on the forest floor, die and disintegrate after they have set their seeds. So do most insects, with the exception of the ants, bees, and wasps, a few of which live through the winter by digging into the earth, or hiding in tree hollows.

Insects go to seed in two ways. They may lay winter eggs in crannies under stones and sticks and fallen leaves; this is the way of crickets, grasshoppers, katydids, and mosquitoes whose eggs are deposited in places that are dry in winter but puddled in spring by rain or melting snow. More commonly, the insect "seed" is a wormlike thing called a larva, or pejoratively a grub or worm, of flies or beetles. A winter grub is fat, tough and inanimate, like a seed in the ground; the larvae of many beetles have discovered that the best winter retreat is under bark and inside wood. When sun warms the bark in early spring these borers bestir themselves, eat wood, and steal a march on summer business.

Some spiders "go to seed" inside a facsimile of a fruit or seed case. This curious resemblance was noted by Jean Henri Fabre, the famous nineteenth-century French naturalist, "the banded spider's nest seems to me like an animal fruit which holds eggs instead of seeds."

The spider lays her eggs in one of the countless cavities in the fallen debris, touches her spinneret all around them, and passes it back and forth as she spins a batch of reddish-brown silky fluid that she beats into a froth with her hind legs. This is wadded around the eggs until they are buried as if in a warm quilt; then the spider changes the color of her thread to transparent silk. When this dries at the touch of air the nest is enclosed for the winter in a white weatherproof case.

In countless curious ways the life of the forest is arrested, with living cells wrought into nuggets of buds and seeds for protection from drying and subzero temperatures. Wonderfully, these passive devices have built-in alarm clocks—a sensitiveness which will cause them to crack open and respond to a particular balance of moisture, temperature and light when winter relaxes its grip.

The fauna of the deciduous forest that are unable to go to seed in the manner of plants and insects, have various recourses. Birds head south for the winter, and many big animals leave the cold, high parts of the forest and move to lower altitudes and areas sheltered from the wind. Little animals dig in or hide in hollow trees. Others find lairs under rocks and fallen tree trunks. Only a few are astir—the grey squirrel, white-footed mouse, cottontail rabbit and white-tailed deer—to write their script in the snow. But many of these feel shy and conspicuous in the daylight of a winter-bright forest and venture out mostly at night.

The spectacular retreat of the forest into winter dormancy is touched off by a soft silent influence. As summer slides by, days grow shorter and nights longer. When the length of the night—the time between sunset and sunrise—reaches a precise number of hours and minutes (even seconds!) a mysterious substance with a powerful influence forms in the green leaves of deciduous trees and bushes. It has the chemical nature of a carbohydrate like sugar, but its molecule has about three times more carbon and hydrogen and less oxygen than a molecule of common sugar. The substance, a hormone, travels down the leaf stem—not via the sap

Come a day in spring, trees that stood "lifeless" all winter are suddenly prickly with life. (Black cherry opens leaf buds.)

Untouched woodland is the finest water-collecting and water-holding system on earth.

Mountain laurel, elegant, strictly American bush of our eastern woodlands. The
State Flower of Connecticut and Pennsylvania.

In early spring before leaves appear, elm flowers explode and throw out ripe pollen. This dramatic event near the tree top is usually unnoticed.

and food delivery tubes, but by diffusing slowly through the juicy cells which surround those pipelines in the stem. The hormone goes exactly the length of the leaf stem, stopping at the point where the stem is attached to the wood of the twig.

At that spot, the hormone causes the soft juicy layer of cells to stiffen and become corky. During late summer weeks, more of this special kind of hormone stuff accumulates at the base of the stem, causing the ring of corkiness to widen. Its center is still open, but it is tightening like a noose around the lifeline of the leaf. The chlorophyll food factory operates uninterruptedly right up to the day appointed for the death of the leaf. But doom casts a shadow ahead—late summer foliage takes on a darker, bluish-green tone, as the corky ring inexorably closes.

The fireworks of fall foliage announces that the leaves of deciduous trees have just been strangled to death. The colorful debacle coincides with chilly weather which slows down the life of the forest, but cold air does not strike the leaves from the trees and warm days of Indian summer do not postpone the performance. It occurs pretty much on schedule.

That vital events in the forest are controlled by hours and minutes of the day and night was an unexpected discovery. It used to be taken for granted that weather had sole charge of the forest cycles. Water, warmth and nourishment do, indeed, build the forest, but changing day-lengths dictate the operations that synchronize the deciduous forest with spring, summer and fall.

Calculations of modern science tell us that the earth's spin is slowing— due to the drag of tides in its oceans and atmosphere—at the rate of 1/100 of a second every thousand years. This spells the end of the forest in some future age, but meanwhile day-length control is serving well. A million years is the geologist's estimate of the Ice Age (Pleistocene). If we take that period as the time when our forest was being modernized and loaded with animals and plants, the earth's spin has since slowed enough to make the 24-hour day 10 seconds longer. This is probably the most trifling adjustment which the clocks of the forest ever made.

The phenomenon of light and darkness control was discovered around 1920 by Dr. W. W. Garner and Dr. H. A. Allard of the Department of Agriculture when they were working with crop plants. They named it "photo-periodism" (light periods). Later research revealed what a rousing breakthrough this was into the secrets of forest and animal life. Even the human animal, which breeds in all seasons, feels vibrations inherited from his ape ancestors who probably acquired a certain genetic trait from "the flowers that bloom in the spring."

The time the sun spends above the horizon during 24 hours decrees when seeds shall crack open and sprout, buds burst, stems elongate, bulbs swell and flowers bloom, putting the act of reproduction into high gear.

The earliest spring flowers have short stems, and can suddenly pop up on the forest floor while leaf buds up in the trees are still tightly closed. The forest floor plants require no time to grow tall, their stamens and pistils are instantly ready to pollinate and form seeds—some of them even before the snow is off the ground. So it is that flowers like trailing arbutus and skunk cabbage flare in February and March when days are short. When days are a few minutes longer, the longer stemmed violets, marsh marigold, early saxifrage, bloodroot, jack-in-the-pulpit, starflower, foam flower and wind anemone bloom in sequence according to the exact day-length of each. But all early spring flowers are short-day flowers.

The long-day flowers are taller still, they have more time to lengthen their stems. They must be located in forest openings and on the edges of ponds, because the forest floor is now too shady. They are flowers such as tall blue lobelia, cardinal-flower, iris, buttercup, pentstemon, St. John's-wort, wild columbine, wild rose. Their blooming schedule is centered on June 21, the longest day of the year.

As days grow shorter in late summer, flowers are taller because they have had more time to grow and set their seeds. Here come milkweed, goldenrod, bull thistle and aster. The declining days of late summer and fall now summon up the tallest flowers; great-stemmed joe-pye-weed, hawkweed, rattlesnake root, and the giants of forest flowers—wild lettuce and angelica, which may have 10-foot stems created in a single season.

I speak of the flowers of the native American deciduous forest. Significantly, the weeds (such as yarrow, wild carrot, mustard, devil's paintbrush) which have invaded plowed fields in man's footsteps, are insensitive to day-length. However, these uncontrolled aliens only beat against the ramparts of the deciduous forest; they do not invade its shady, time-perfected sanctuaries.

The tiny inconspicuous flowers of the forest trees are even more sensitive to day-length than those on the forest floor. Their tree structure is there, the buds have been packed for six months. Those buds are taut springs ready to be released. Like the little flowers on the forest floor, the flowers on the tree's highest twigs are short-day flowers. Their extreme sensitivity to just a few seconds difference in day-length is seen in the way they spark stamens and pistils in the same order every year, swiftly through the spring.

Willow flowers are the first to throw off the grip of winter; pussy willows are emblems of spring. They are followed by silver maple, red maple and elm, in that order. (The trees flower before their leaf buds stir.) Then come sugar maple, poplar, birch—with their leaf buds so close on the heels of their flower buds that the former open the very day after the flowers wither. Oak, beech and sweet gum await a slightly longer day, and their leaves unfurl while their flowers are out, as though the trees must catch up with the parade. These are followed by walnut and hickory, the last of the short-day trees.

In late spring, the long-day tree flowers bloom—basswood, cherry, crab apple, locust. This makes sense because they are insect pollinated and must wait for their friends—in contrast to short-day tree flowers that are pollinated by the wind. In the long perspective of forest evolution, insect-pollinated flowers and trees are newcomers who either joined the forest after coming from warmer climates, or evolved their alliances with insects in recent times.

The changing lengths of day control the reproduction of the animal life of the forest as well as its trees and flowers. The gradually lengthening days of early spring stir gonads. This is the irresistible impulse for bird migration. Birds which headed south when the leaves fell are impelled to head north again when longer days hold a hint of spring. Their glands are stimulated by the sunlight to produce hormones, which travel to the gonads, and these forthwith alert the birds to go north and mate in a berry-and-insect-laden paradise, as their ancestors did. At the same time, gonads prodded by the right length of day, cause the plumage of birds to take on bright colors—birds are daylight breeders, their estrus can be visibly signaled.

Thus, as the days of spring slide by, the forest is repopulated with nervous, articulate and colorful birds. Some are transient. Ducks, geese, cranes, herons and cormorants stop en route to swim and wade in the marshes and shallow ponds of the forest. Some stay all summer—warblers, hummingbirds, pigeons, grouse, perching birds and songsters. Others are birds of prey—eagles, hawks, ospreys and vultures, attracted by fresh, young flesh.

The reproductive influence of day-length penetrates even the fresh waters of the forest. Minnows, the largest group of fresh-water fish in the American forest, await a long day to spawn—some time after the ice is gone from their lakes and streams. But brook trout wait until the short days of late fall. Lengthening days of spring convert sticklebacks from salt- to fresh-water fish, and short days of late summer and fall impel them to turn to become salt-water fish again. Juvenile salmon, which are fresh-water fish in an inland lake, are compelled by a long day in June to leave the place of their birth and take a long dangerous journey to breed in the ocean.

Day length stirs gonads throughout the forest. It puts ferrets, weasels and raccoons on the prowl for mates. Even cold-blooded lizards, turtles, crayfish and snails seem to have romantic urges.

When day is short and night is long in late fall, a crash followed by a grinding sound is heard in the forest just at sunset. It is the collision and wrenching of the antlers of two bucks locked in combat. Their rutting time, too, comes when the sun is above the horizon for a certain number of days and hours. The urge to breed assembles all the female white-tailed deer in estrus—which had been scattered far and wide in the forest —at the same time and place.

Then the shy white-tailed deer suddenly become excited; the males strut and lift their heads high to show how strong and tall they are and how majestic their antlers. In this aggressive mood, when one buck meets another, they lower their heads, then charge, and push. The crash of antlers is not so much a battle cry as a mating call. The does who are attracted to the neighborhood, act bored while they wait for the pushing match to end—usually in a draw. After that ceremony, each buck takes a doe. The chemistry of day-length has brought the opposite sexes together. So the shy and voiceless deer reproduce, in another time-honored ritual of the ancient forest.

White-tailed deer of the eastern deciduous forest have relatives, the wapiti, widely scattered in the deep dark conifer forests of the western mountains. On his rutting day, a wapiti bull comes out of the depths at sundown and climbs to a high commanding point that is free of trees to let go an unearthly bugling. The call starts with a reverberating roar like a steam safety valve letting go, then, rising in pitch to a scream, it soars and echoes through the mountains.

In contrast to birds, which flaunt colors for daylight breeding, a female moth, who is a nighttime breeder, exudes a strong scent that drifts through the forest. This has been known to summon a male two miles away. It duplicates the role of certain white flowers of the forest which are ripe to be pollinated at night and to that end release their fragrance only in the dark.

Day-length touches off reproduction throughout the forest in the spring, and cuts off such activity in the fall. Bear, fox and mink swiftly acquire their winter pelages, birds moult, the stately antlers of white-tailed deer and wapiti fall off.

Here in the deciduous forest is a mysterious and wonderful force that controls many and various actions according to the day of the year and the special needs of a species. It synchronizes the dazzling diversity of forest life with the earth's rotation which varies with every mile of latitude. The living clocks in trees may be reset every day, every hour, every minute, by the interplay of daylight and darkness—*independent of the caprices of weather*. A cold or rainy spell may delay some events (such as the opening of buds, the unfolding of flowers) a little beyond the day which calls for them. But such delays are temporary, isolated and local. The important point is that they cannot occur *before* the right day-length comes. *After* that, the bud will open, the leaf unfurl and the seed sprout at the first moment that conditions permit. Other events scheduled for a later day may occur at the same time as the slightly delayed events, and thus the forest is quickly and quietly put back on precise schedule. The deciduous forest is synchronized in every phase with the pendulum of the seasons, and squared with the latitude.

Unwavering control, perpetual from age to age, is essential to the evolution of this kind of forest. If such a vast array of complex life were geared entirely to weather, then trees, bushes, flowers, insects, fruits and animals, could never have sorted out their various lives and coordinated them to create a symphony. The famous caprices of the thermometer, of rain and sunshine, would have created chaos rather than rhythm.

Whether by master plan or by supernal luck, the fundamental phases of forest life such as reproduction, growth and leaf fall are geared to celestial forces—to the rotation of the earth on its axis, which causes the rising and setting of the sun, and to the rate of travel of the earth on the ecliptic, that causes the sliding of the seasons north and south across the latitudes.

This phenomenon discovered recently by modern science, was not overlooked by ancient man, as revealed in *The Chhandogya Upanishad* (India, *circa* 750 B.C.): "When yonder sun was born there were shouts and hurrahs. All beings rose to greet it. At its rising and at its every return there are shouts and hurrahs, all beings and all desires rise up to greet it."

chapter six

Wood

BOTH the deciduous and conifer forests of America are receiving much attention nowadays. Survivors of pre-white-man forests, plus considerable second growth, woodlot, and plantation trees are being strained to the utmost by the surge of popularity of wood.

Wood has acquired a very modern look. Nearly 2 billion square yards of fabrics per year are woven out of cellulose, the substance of wood cells. Streams are jammed with logs crunching and jerking on their way to pulp mills to be transformed into 40 million tons per year of paper and cardboard. It takes the annual growth of 252 acres of forest to make the paper for a single Sunday edition of one New York newspaper.

How fantastically modern *tall oil* has suddenly become. It is a foamy, yellow-brown lignin "soup" which got its name from a word given it by Swedes employed in paper mills in Minnesota. The Swedish word for the annoying waste liquor sounded like "tall oil," and tall oil it became throughout the paper industry. Today it makes soaps, sizes, and cold water paints. And lignin (25 percent of the volume of wood) is used to bind highway blacktops, in paste for laying linoleum, to increase the life of car batteries, and as vanilla flavoring in ice cream, candy and cake.

Wood popularity is also measured by 40 billion board feet of lumber turned out by 50 thousand saw mills each year. In addition, there are myriad wood products, each made from a particular tree. For example:

baseball bats, oars and ladders from the ash tree. Venetian blinds and picture frames from basswood. Gun stocks from black walnut. Choice furniture from cherry. Mallet heads and pulleys from dogwood. Wagon wheel hubs from elm. Piano, organ and accordion keys from holly. Fine furniture and athletic equipment from maple. Policemen's clubs from Osage orange. Toys, toothpicks, and conductor's batons from birch. Shoe lasts, shuttles, and golf club heads from persimmon. Excelsior, butter tubs, and fruit crates from poplar. Axe handles and sled runners from hickory. Radio and television cabinet veneer from sweet gum (under the pseudonyms of satin walnut, hazelwood, or hazel pine). Butcher's blocks from sycamore. Inside bureau drawers and artists' drawing boards from tulip tree. Floors, heavy construction, fine furniture from oak. Charcoal and baskets from willow.

We have not yet counted the strapping logs of oak, beech and maple in the processions of a billion railroad ties. The elasticity of wood lends incomparable vitality to a track that must "give" before the terrific impact of an onrushing train while safely bearing the tonnage. Nor have we mentioned 600 million posts used each year along 15 million miles of fencing. Just how *modern* is this extraordinary material which trees quietly concoct for their trunks?

Once upon a time, land life did not exist. It has been said, "From the standpoint of a jelly fish, life on dry land is sheer nonsense." But evolution not only does everything possible; given time, it does the virtually impossible. When the population explosion among seaweeds, ferns and mosses at the edge of the sea and in boggy estuaries became intolerable some 400 million years ago, cells invented wood, and the first tree ventured to live a few feet inland.

The seaweeds, ferns, and mosses of the pre-tree world were imbued with green chlorophyll to make food in sunshine out of water and air, but their bodies were prostrate, flabby, floating. The towering feat of wood was to build a firm, enduring structure that could lift the green parts into the sunshine and air, flex in the wind, spring back into position after bending, not dry out and collapse, and pipe water from moisture below to the green parts above. This great invention broke down the barriers at the water's edge and forests led the way out of the water and across the land for all bushes and flowers, insects, birds and animals. Sediments of that world, when continents were without animal life, closed over the first trees so that they left their imprints in rocks for us to see 400 million years later. The sketches in stone have been unearthed in eastern Canada, Maine, Czechoslovakia and Norway.

To us who see trees with the luxurious equipment that millions of years of evolution have bestowed upon them, the first tree looks scrawny, unfortunate, hardly deserving to be called a tree. It was about 2½ feet tall and its trunk was half an inch thick; it had no true roots, no leaves, no buds and it produced no seeds. Its name is *Psilophytum,* Greek for "naked plant," referring to its lack of foliage. Yet, as an exhibit in a museum its label might state that this paltry pilot model was the most momentous thing that ever inhabited the land.

The wood cells mounted a tough vibrant little trunk, which branched and rebranched with upreaching slender twigs, each tipped with a small tight spiral like the crozier of a fern. The twigs were studded with lumps, showing that this tree reproduced by spores. The silhouette was simple and graceful.

Instead of roots (where there was no soil) the base of the trunk was a cushion of tangled branches, that probably collected moisture from sodden clumps of ferns and mosses or bunches of seaweed. The cushion steadied the tree in an upright position, and, woody like the trunk, the tangle did not collapse when exposed to the sun.

When hurricane waves flung gobs of seaweed well beyond the high-water line where the wrack settled permanently into a hollow, and naked plant grew upon it, high and dry behind the dunes, wood as an invention became a success.

Contemplating the scene in our mind's eye, the little tree looks lonely in a very empty world. It is a fair day; the sea is calm and blue. The land is low, rolling rock, with no shadows when the sun is high. Land and sea are the same emptiness, blended together in a bluish mist and sultry silence. No gulls squawk. No terns wheel. No sandpipers run back and forth with the sliding waves. Nothing blows in the wind. The only motion is the heaving of sea waves, their breaking and their spreading on the sand, and the doomlike creeping of the tides. Although it is a tree's nature never to grow alone (trees have an inevitable tendency to form forest), for naked tree there would be neither forest shadows nor forest soil. We can visualize naked trees scattered widely and thrusting upward from black clumps of wrack that frame the broad bay. Their little green sticks might also be seen a little farther inland in shallow gullies. Their jaunty silhouettes poke up from clumps of ferns and moss where rain water has puddled in depressions of the rock. The stark geometry of naked tree's world, the eerie stillness where even the winds, with nothing to whistle through, were silent, the lonely, abruptly vertical, little trees like exclamation points in jejune surroundings, suggest a contemporary abstract painting.

Like fog rolling in, the ages blotted out the world of the dauntless little naked tree, while its descendants with heavy wood trunks and leaves led forests to colonize the land, where flaccid plants would fail. Mosses, liverworts and prostrate ferns have no roots with which to crack rock. Small plants cannot mobilize resources to invade great continents; they lack the immensity of foliage, fruits and wood to store duff for humus of forest soil. Their kind of life could not climb the sun-swept slopes of mountain sides. Their places must be glistening wet. They must cling to damp depressions where their spores can find water to swim in without a moment's delay.

Little animals that came to hide in seaweed wrack along the beach and in the cool shady mats of mosses and ferns were only half out of water. These were salamanders, centipedes, scorpions and a miscellany of creatures like sow bugs, mites and tardigrades. These could venture a few feet outside their little corals but would then scamper back into shade and moisture. Gills of snails and crabs can function both in water and air. Salamanders and centipedes have air-breathing apparatus. In the age of naked tree, fish had pockets on their gills from which they absorbed oxygen.

Seaweeds rolling in the waves along the beach, and exposed at low tide, were taking their oxygen both under water and in the air.

The struggle of sea life to gain the land in that distant age is replayed on beaches today where crabs come out and contest with flies and beetles for bits of carcass in the wrack. Goby fish live peacefully in mud when the tide goes out; other gobies, using their paired fins like crutches, hobble on the land on a rainy day to hunt insects. The incredible hippa sand bugs have maintained their place between land and sea for millions of years by digging to keep from being toppled in an onrushing wave and then popping up to spread their food-catching antennae in the reverse current flowing back to the sea.

All of which suggests what land life on this planet would probably have been like if wood had not been invented. Gravity, not air-breathing, was the chief obstacle to colonizing the land. Anybody who enjoys diving and swimming knows the feeling of buoyancy in the water in contrast to heaviness on land. Seaweeds never solved the problem of gravity. They lie prostrate when exposed to the air at low tide. Liverworts are flat as pancakes. Mosses are low-growing and creeping. Primitive ferns are prone, although in the course of time ferns stiffened their stems and lifted their fronds above the ground in graceful arches.

When wood was innovated, tree bodies became so robust that they could pit life against the rocks of ages. It is an extraordinary creation, wood—this biological organization that so deftly solved the problem of gravity in behalf of living cells and then moved steadily forward to create forests.

The great revolution wrought by wood did not alter in the slightest the basic nature of the living cell. It only directed protoplasm with its time-honored proteins to compound new chemicals so that it could leave the sea. The size and career of each living cell that went ashore to make trees was the same as those in the sea. The droplet of protoplasm still had to be kept immersed in water so that it could exchange oxygen and energy with its surroundings every split second.

Wood carried the delicate living cell out of the water into the open air without disturbing its watery nature. Wood created a solidity around protoplasm, enabling it to erect a structure that would resist the crushing weight of gravity, while keeping constantly wet even when lifted up hundreds of feet into the sun and air. A stick of wood, 12 inches long, 2 inches wide and one inch deep, set vertically, can support a downward thrust of twenty tons.

The first bit of wood on this planet may have taken epochs to assemble. Cellulose is made by linking together 120 molecules of glucose (sugar) in a chain. Each molecule of cellulose has the same number of carbon, hydrogen and oxygen atoms, combined in the same pattern as starch, but with one peculiar difference. In starch, glucose molecules all face the same way like soldiers on parade. In cellulose, every other molecule faces in the opposite direction. This makes cellulose strong and durable in contrast to starch, which is easily dissolved. The little cellulose chains are then laid parallel and arranged in loose bundles of 60 each. Finally, 6 bundles are loosely twisted together in spirals like fibers in twine. To this point we have cellulose, not wood. The spiraling twine is flimsy. It could not erect a pillar strong enough to support the weight of a tree.

It is important that the chain of cellulose molecules be loosely put together and that its threads in turn be loosely twisted. This reveals the genius of the power that invented wood. The spaces between the cellulose threads and bundles are filled with *lignin,* a substance which is transparent in fresh wood, giving it a golden tint, but darkens when exposed to air and light. Lignin turns cellulose into wood. It is a complicated chemical that cannot be classified by molecular weight. As recently as 1948 chemists were unable to agree on its peculiar formula. It contains benzene; it is aromatic, breathing the delicious fragrance that comes from sawed wood, and it has the delicate flavor of vanilla. When living cells interlaced their cellulose twine with lignin, a material was concocted which had the tensile strength of steel, the rigidity to rise straight up and support tons of matter, and a rugged elasticity that could withstand the strain of great winds.

In producing wood, living cells turn themselves into dead wood cells. While the cells are dying, their chemical laboratories must be very busy. The transformation starts where a fabric of cells have delicate, transparent walls woven of cellulose threads. The thin membrane of one cell with its whisper of cellulose is in contact with the walls of neighboring cells. An isolated cell never turns into wood. It must be stimulated by the pressure of cells around it. The pressing together of cell walls causes a peculiar chemical, pectin, to form and this cements them together tightly but pliantly. Pectin is an acid containing gum arabic and methyl alcohol which gels under pressure. The tough flexibility of young wood is seen in swaying limbs and fluttering of leaves.

While cells are being welded in this way, their chemical activities are in high gear. Their protoplasm is absorbing water, pressures are building up, the thin fresh elastic walls are expanding. But because of the crowd of surrounding cells the youngest central cells expand lengthwise more than sidewise. Twigs are lengthening. The trunk is mounting. The tree is growing.

While elongating, the cells are steadily transforming themselves into wood by spinning more cellulose to line their original walls. Then the cellulose forms a third layer between the two layers. In perfect synchronization wood cells are welded together; their cellulose walls are permeated with lignin, the wall of each finished wood cell is laminated like plywood with three layers—actually six layers, when you add the three layers of the neighboring cells. This is, indeed, a strong construction.

What happens to the living protoplasm of cells which turn into wood?

When a cell begins to transform itself into a microscopic splinter of wood, a bubble forms in its protoplasm and the bubble steadily enlarges as the protoplasm is used up in forming the three-ply walls. The steadily-enlarging bubble shows that the cell is dying on schedule. In the final stages of becoming wood, only a thin layer of protoplasm lines the walls and when this is used up, the spark of life goes out. There is now a minute hollow splinter of wood.

In building a tree trunk, the hollow, needlelike wood cells are joined end to end. Their side walls are peppered with tiny round pits where they are separated by a thin perforated membrane through which water can pass back and forth between adjacent cells. Thus the wood needles act like tubes that carry sap from the deepest root to the highest twig.

The pits through which sap passes from cell to cell are scattered irregularly along cell walls, but necessarily precisely in opposite pairs between touching cells. This is one of those gentle miracles that make a tree. It seems that a cell may not locate pits in its own walls until it "knows" the exact locations of its neighbor's pits!

The instant a cell's work is completed and its protoplasm is gone, the dead wood cell will never move from its original location in the trunk, limb, twig, or root.

Wood mobilized fantastic capabilities. The trees it built seized the land with a mighty grasp of roots and stood their ground when assaulted by brutal hurricanes, cloudbursts and violent changes of temperature. Thanks to fast moving, air-borne seeds which wooden trees perfected to insure their survival, the forests the trees made could defy the ages by dodging and fleeing inundations of land by the sea, the rise and fall of mountains, fiery streams of lava and overpowering glaciers.

A tree is a tower of leaves tier above tier, erected on a skeleton of branches and twigs supported by a central pillar. Its proportion and strength are precisely adjusted to the weight of its every part, from light slender branch tips to massive pedestal. The pillar (and each branch and twig) is an extremely elongated cone, seemingly a cylinder, made by tightly fitting together a succession of increasingly larger wood cones manufactured in succession through the years. Each year's new wood cone fits tightly over last year's.

As this proceeds through decades and centuries, the tree's body, weighing tons, is slowly lifted against the relentless pull of gravity. But there is nothing ponderous about it. A growing tree is buoyant and serene. These largest organisms alive on earth absorb the quiet, pervading power of sunlight, store this power systematically throughout their frames, then put it to work in an orderly way without ado. As long as it lives, a tree never ceases to lengthen its roots, widen its trunk, and reach a little higher.

Living bodies with wood have immortality compared to all other living things. The General Sherman tree in Sequoia National Park has fitted 3,800 annual fresh wood sheaths, one around another, until the diameter of its trunk today is 36 feet. The lowest branch of General Sherman is 150 feet above the ground. It is 6½ feet in diameter and more than 150 feet long. This branch alone is larger than the largest American elm. Imagine the awesome leverage of a big elm tree held *horizontally* 150 feet above the ground!

Tree tonnage is not lifted above the earth in the sense of being upended or hoisted. Cells at the peak of the trunk and the tips of the twigs are born from cells already there, and thus the tree trunk flows upward and the branches flow outward. No tons of weight are hoisted. A tree lifts microscopic weights with microscopic forces in microscopic cells which inch the tree toward the sky.

Growth power in a tree is generated when cells possessed of high chemical energy suddenly absorb water and swell. This power multiplies by combining millions of cells in tissues where they exert their energy in unison. In growing trunks and limbs, the energy expended by the elongating of one cell is multiplied by billions, trillions and billions times trillions, according to the number of cells mobilized at each location. This organized power of protoplasm can not only counteract gravity easily but can enable flaccid tree roots to break into heavy sewer tiles and buckle concrete pavement in a miniature earthquake.

The tiny succulent shoot of a germinating seed, which appears so tender and weak, will push aside sizable stones and debris. This shoot, the beginning trunk, usually breaks through a hard surface by assuming the bent posture of Atlas holding up the world. It keeps its tip underground for an extra day or two while it heaves upward in the form of an arch, thus doubling its lifting power. A root shoot emerging from an acorn that happens to be lying on the surface of the ground does not stab downward like a dagger; it spirals and enters the ground easily with a corkscrew twist.

A few years ago a botanist came upon a larch tree on a mountain side whose seed had originally sprouted in the crack of a big granite boulder. The grain of the boulder ran horizontally, which forced the root of the tree to grow horizontally through it, splitting the rock to open a passage. The root had to expand as well as elongate, and the expansion of the growing root had actually jacked up the upper half of the boulder, which was carefully calculated to weigh about 1½ tons. The boulder, poised exactly on top of the root, had been lifted 12 inches, the diameter of the thickest part of the root.

The first scientific report of the growth power of expanding and elongating cells created a sensation, and not only among botanists. In 1875, a Massachusetts farmer, curious about the growing power of expanding apples, melons and squashes, harnessed a squash to a weight-lifting device which had a dial like a grocer's scale to indicate the pressure exerted by the expanding fruit. As the days passed, he kept piling on counterbalancing weight; he could hardly believe his eyes when he saw his vegetables quietly exerting a lifting force of 5 thousand pounds per square inch. When nobody believed him, he set up exhibits of harnessed squashes and invited the public to come and see. The *Annual Report of the Massachusetts Board of Agriculture,* 1875, reported: "Many thousands of men, women, and children of all classes of society visited it. *Mr. Penlow* watched it day and night, making hourly observations; *Professor Parker* was moved to write a poem about it; *Professor Seelye* declared that he positively stood in awe of it."

We witness growth when buds open in the spring. The branches are inert and bare one day, and suddenly, after a few hours of warm sunlight, leaves have unfurled and little tassels dangle all over the canopy. The expansion of the trunk is imperceptible, but the result of horizontal growth beneath the bark is revealed by the dead, cracked and furrowed, outer bark.

The most lively and strenuous action in a tree takes place down in its roots, where root tips explore microscopic spaces and crannies between grains of soil. They make their way between small stones and into cracks of large stones; they detour around obstructions; they twist, turn, double back and spread a maze of branches in the soil. The insatiable root tips are guided in their wanderings by specks of moisture which attract them like magnets.

We have noted how cells magnify power by working in unison. In root tips, they are organized in regiments which coordinate their activities. The outermost point of a root tip is shod with a helmet of tough rigid cells that serve as both a battering ram and a wedge. Immediately behind this helmet, other cells are rapidly dividing and multiplying. They are producing the materials for bigger roots. Behind these, still other cells are stretching lengthwise, giving push to the helmet's battering ram. The extending root cells are growing in the same manner as other cells high above them and far away in the outer world of the air where twigs are lengthening.

Inside an extending cell a chemical influence causes it to absorb water and distend. Pressure mounts, the inflow continues and the interwoven cellulose threads of its expanding wall are stretched to the breaking point. Still the intake of water persists. Where the cell wall yields or tears, new cellulose threads are quickly produced and woven into the wall, mending it and making it larger. In this way, an extending cell, without dividing, increases its volume more than twenty times. It becomes three times as wide and seven times as long as it was before it began to extend.

Underground in the root tip, in an area just behind the extending cells, events unique in all the pageantry of life are taking place. The root tip is headed for a spot of moisture and now, at the hint of water, like a hunting dog scenting game, the cells immediately behind the extending cells produce countless innumerable cottony hairs which elongate so fast that, under a microscope, they can be seen to be growing. Each cottony hair, zigzagging between soil particles, moves toward a soil particle that has a film of moisture on its surface. When the root hair touches the moisture it broadens and grasps the particle as a catcher's mitt traps a baseball. Swiftly the hair sucks in the moisture and, after the water on that particle is absorbed, the delicate sucking thread simply melts away. Meanwhile, the root tip continues to push its helmet a little farther through the soil. As it proceeds, forward root hairs are shriveling, but behind them myriads of fresh hairs are springing out to suck in more water from more particles.

No one can count the astronomical numbers of root hairs working for a large tree. The root-hair galaxy works swiftly; it is as volatile as vapor. It would be impossible to get all this evanescent living matter in the root system of a tree out of the ground, wash it clean of soil, and count the root hairs on a square millimeter of surface.

The best official record of numbers and lengths of root hairs comes from painstaking research of the water-collecting apparatus of some farm crops. An experiment was set up in which a vigorous grass, winter rye, was grown in fertile, well-watered, well-aerated soil in a greenhouse, under laboratory conditions. This permitted soil to be removed with scientific care, exposing root hairs for counting and measuring. The report states that 14 billion hairs, with an end-to-end length of 6 thousand miles, were crammed into one cubic inch of soil. This was the water collecting apparatus of one grass plant!

chapter seven

River of Sap

A TREE stands motionless. It is nerveless and silent, its trunk seems solid and it contains no organs in the usual sense. Yet a tree is alive from the cap of its deepest root to the tip of its highest twig.

The key to a tree's efficiency as an organism lies in the unique fact that only about one percent of the bulk of a tree's body consists of live cells that require constant maintenance. Comparatively little energy is expended in doing a big job. Only a few cells, relative to the size of the tree, must be supplied with food, water and oxygen.

Moreover, a tree's arrangements for reproducing are superb. Its sex organs are very small considering that they propagate the biggest things alive, but they are designed so precisely that they possess basic qualities of art—utility, fitness, economy and the perfect adaptation of the means to the end. These reproductive organs are created swiftly, produce myriads of embryos in a matter of a few days and vanish. Then, on schedule, usually a year later, entirely fresh, new sets of sex organs bloom all over the periphery of the tree's canopy where direct rays of sunlight provide energy.

Although wood cells are not alive, they are entirely different from ordinary dead organic matter. They do not collapse into a shapeless mess. They hold their shape, and they are precisely fitted together to make an operating mechanism which does not require food and servicing like

83

living cells. Barring accidents, wood cells playing their roles in a tree's body are shielded from the bacteria of decay by the sheath of bark; they can endure for centuries without weakening.

The success of a tree as an organism depends on the strategic location of its living cells. Imagine that by some sorcery all wood, bark and non-living material in a tree, and even the ground which conceals its roots, were to disappear and leave only the living cells standing in utter naked-ness. A shimmering phantom would be revealed in which every tiny detail of the tree could be seen. The trunk has lost its massive ruggedness. It is a tall slender cone, as delicate and transparent as a soap bubble. Its interior is void, except for spectral silvery ribbons of wood rays that run horizontally between the outer surface and the center of the trunk, fading out at various lengths.

The leaf canopy of this ghost is a silvery mist made by living cells crowded together in buds and leaves. The root system of the tree, at a casual glance, reflects the form of its canopy, with its intricate network of branches. The "foliage" of the root system consists of root hairs which alternately bloom and fade, undulating like a shimmering aurora borealis.

This is no purely imaginary vision. It tells the arrangement of the living cells in the tree's body. A tree's diagram is often compared to that of a river system. On a map of the United States you can see the outline of a colossal tree straddling the center of this continent with its outermost twigs in the Appalachian and Rocky Mountains attached to its largest limbs, the Ohio and Missouri Rivers. Countless are the twigs and branches of this magnificent water-collecting system. Its trickles, brooks and creeks, in perfect sequence, increase steadily in size as they lead into the central trunk of the Mississippi River.

A watershed and a tree have similar silhouettes because they are both created by fluids moving under the influence of gravity. But here the comparison ends. Watershed patterns are two-dimensional and their lines have capricious bends because they are etched on the surface of uneven ground. Tree patterns are three-dimensional and tend to be symmetrical because they are traced in the air by radiations of light.

Each day the radiant energy of the sun first strikes a tree from the east, then floods it from a constantly higher angle as the sun travels up and over the crown of the tree. Then descending, it paints the opposite side of the tree with sunlight, until the light is suddenly shut off at the western horizon. A tree is molded in the open air by the curving touch of light.

The diagrams of watersheds and trees are different in an even more arresting way. In a river system, water flows according to the pull of gravity; the sap in a tree flows in exactly the opposite direction, against gravity.

Thus, a tree can be imagined to be an upside-down river system. Its source is in the ground where root hairs and rootlets are the trickles, brooks and rivers. The water collected in the black earth flows through channels of increasing size and converges into the main stream at the base of the trunk. Then instantly, emerging from the ground, a column of water is formed that flows silently straight up into the air. The canopy of the tree then becomes the mouth of this upside down river, where its water is released into the atmosphere as invisible vapor.

This is not a matter of a little moisture slowly creeping up through wood. A large tree transports water by the ton. Logs are heavy. A short section of a single Douglas fir log must be hauled in a 10-ton truck. It takes muscle even to heave split logs onto a campfire. About half of the weight of a fresh log is water, and the percentage is much greater in other parts of the tree; fruits like apples and cherries are 85 percent water. Leaves and twigs on trees during the growing season are 80 percent water. Singly, these items seem light, but a squat apple tree may have 100 thousand leaves, and a towering elm 6 million. The river of a tree has a wide and generous mouth through which, on the little apple tree, four gallons of water are expelled every hour. At this rate, an acre of apple orchard, planted with the usual forty trees, will collect from the ground and discharge into the air 480 tons of water a month. It is impossible to estimate how much water is lifted and discharged into the air by a towering elm.

What can be said about the volume of water flowing upward in a lush forest? This answer would be more closely related to a Noachian flood than to trees standing quietly in the sunlight.

Ninety-nine percent of the water which streams upward in a tree trunk is thrown away into the air from the top of the tree—a mere one percent is used in the tree's living cells. This one percent is enough to provide the hydrogen needed for the manufacture of carbohydrates by the leaves, for the protoplasm of cells, and for blowing up cells which are about to divide or elongate. But why only one percent? Is this not awfully inefficient? Why all the energetic water collecting and lifting?

It is tempting to think that trees are rendering a benign service in promoting the cycle of water in which all life participates. This, however, is an all-too-human attitude toward forests. The fact is that all forms of

Each kind of tree has its own funny face on the twig just below the winter bud. Left, mockernut hickory. Right, elm.

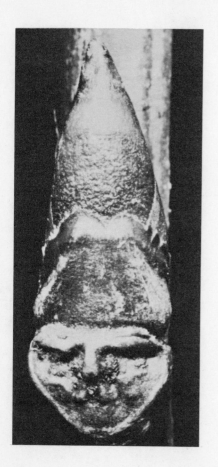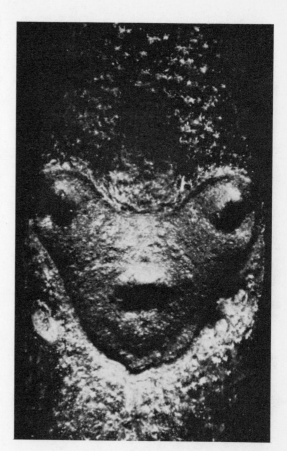

Faces are marks left on the twig after leaf fall, where leaf stem was attached to twig. Left, poplar. Right, hobblebush viburnum.

The flow of this big trunk rising out of the soil is a "movie still" of the way trees grow. (Arborvitae, Natural Bridge, Va.)

Larch and bald cypress are the only conifers that shed their foliage in the fall. This larch is shown covered with fresh, soft needles in springtime.

The indomitable nature of some wild trees is expressed by this pitch pine fighting fierce winds and bitter winter cold on the rocky highest spot in Connecticut.

life are utterly and completely selfish. Trees are not collecting water and laying up food for cattails and water lilies, Canada geese and beavers—not even for us.

As I ponder sap rising in the trees, I descry something profoundly interesting. Here is a replay of the forces which created life in the sea.

We are told that the first living cells were concocted in shallow estuaries where the vital elements of carbon, hydrogen, oxygen, nitrogen and certain minerals were dissolved and mixed in gentle currents. These elements had been locked up in granite and volcanic rocks and in atmospheric molecules when the earth's crust hardened. Set free by dissolution in water, the atoms became magnetized—what chemists call ions—packed with chemical energy and ready to make all sorts of combinations. Whisked around in currents, stirred by tides and sunlight, the magnetized atoms clung together or jerked apart according to the plus and minus signs of their electricity. Collisions through an infinity of time combined elements in peculiar and dynamic molecules which had not existed in the fire-and-rock ages of the earth. Thus, protoplasm, protein and chlorophyll appeared in sun warmed tidal pools and arms of the sea and life stuff slowly evolved.

The water in the trunk of a tree is an arm of that primordial sea. But unlike the atoms in the primordial sea, the combinations of elements and mineral ions in tree sap are not haphazard. The form of a tree, its posture, the strict controls of its currents, are predetermined by its genes.

Vital forces are so strongly organized in a tree, the pattern of growth so firmly fixed in its genes, that molecular arrangements which took epochs to assemble in the primeval seas appear in a tree like magic, in a few hours. Elements in the streaming tree sap sort themselves out and combine in the right proportions at the right places.

For instance, only one atom of magnesium is attached to a specific number of carbon, hydrogen, nitrogen and oxygen atoms to make a molecule of green chlorophyll. Proteins are even more complex, with precisely counted hundreds and thousands of nitrogen, carbon, oxygen and hydrogen atoms—and perhaps a touch of sulfur or phosphorus—which are strung in a certain order like links in a long chain.

About forty different elements are used to build and activate a tree, including copper, manganese, boron, iodine, aluminum, mercury, cobalt, zinc and silver. Some of these are very scarce where trees grow, but in the copious stream inside a tree trunk, as in the currents of the primeval sea, even the rarest elements turn up. The moment underground water is sucked through the walls of root hairs and starts to flow through the labyrinthine channels of the roots toward the trunk of the tree, it becomes sap with a fine and rare quality. It is purer than water in a mountain spring, for it contains no bacteria and no organic matter. These have been carefully filtered out by the cell walls.

Here is, indeed, an arresting paradox. Trees flourish the more in fertile humus teeming with bacteria and packed with organic matter from decayed cells. Yet all bacteria and organic matter are excluded from the water that enters the roots and mounts the trunk. It is this that makes tree sap like an arm of the primeval sea. In that sea the elements of life were available in loose, easy-to-use molecules of water and air in which were dissolved atoms of phosphorus and sulfur, and all the minerals essential to life. Living cells could select for their protoplasm precisely the elements needed. Even the rare minerals—copper, manganese, mercury, cobalt, silver—came floating along in the currents sooner or later in free atomic form. So it was in the sea water where life originated; so it is in the sap of a tree.

Fertile humus is a stewpot holding concentrations of the elements—particularly atoms of sulfur, phosphorus and minerals—that had been assembled in the cells of all sorts of living things. In the humus they are being released by decay, and dissolved in the ground water. Solutions of their freed atoms permeate the soil where they are picked up by the tree roots. They will flow to the top of the canopy where they bring their offerings of elements to living cells in leaves, buds and flowers. They will bathe all the cells in the gossamer sheath under the bark. Fertile humus simply increases the strength of those solutions, most importantly of nitrogen, phosphorus, sulfur and the minerals.

What about the famous maple sugar sap? Here is a carbohydrate, not contained in the primeval sea. This is the result of the stoppage of sap flow in winter. Left standing in the trunk, sugar from surrounding maple wood becomes dissolved in the sap. But this dilution of its pure mineral quality is only temporary. Sugar in sap is of no use to the tree, although it is much enjoyed by people.

If water in a tree trunk is an arm of the ancient sea, why is it not salty? When life began 2½ billion years ago the ocean contained no sodium chloride (table salt) as it does today. Sodium is inert when combined with chlorine in water. It does not evaporate. Other minerals with more chemical energy evaporate, leave the sea as water vapor and fall on the land as rain or snow to be redissolved in ground water and picked up again by roots. But not sodium. The time of its residence in the oceans is equal to the age of the oceans. Thus through the ages the seas have become saltier as more sodium dissolves out of the earth's crust and accumulates in the ocean basins.

Stray molecules of sodium chloride which have not yet reached the ocean are wandering around in the soil almost everywhere. These traces of sodium are taken in by root hairs along with other mineral salts. They ride the river of sap from the roots to the leaves and are expelled in the air, forever shunned by the living cells of the tree. Sodium enough to give sap the slightest taste of saltiness would be poisonous to trees.

The word salt in the chemical sense includes all minerals dissolved out of rocks, although they do not taste salty, and in this sense only is tree sap salty. Particular mineral salts—the same ones that were in the water of the primordial ocean and played a part in the invention of the living cell—are today performing spectacular feats in trees. The tree which we see is made *with* carbohydrates but *by* mineral salts.

The invisible elements (both nonmineral and mineral) sucked from microscopic particles of soil and borne in the tree's sap are the most energetic elements. Some of them fly together, fly apart, poison, sting, burn, and explode. They are the elements that excited superstition and magic when the alchemists played with them in the Middle Ages.

Nitrogen, which sleeps in the atmosphere like an inert block of space, has its nature suddenly changed when it is stricken out of the air by flashes of lightning or eaten by bacteria in the soil. Either of these events turns nitrogen into burning ammonia. When an electric current is passed through nitrogen, it glows with a yellow light for some time after the electricity is turned off. Nitrogen in the form of an acid has terrifying power and is the stuff of high explosives. Such is the key element of protein in trees.

A protein molecule is a chemical that behaves as though it were alive. It grows and folds itself in certain ways. It makes protoplasm dynamic. Protein combined with DNA (the molecule of inheritance) in the nucleus of every living cell holds the code of the tree's life, spells out its species— the height of its trunk, the shape of its leaves, its kind of flowers and seeds. An enzyme is nitrogen's masterpiece. Enzymes direct every living act. For example, enzymes produced in buds at the tips of twigs travel the full length of the tree—several hundred feet in tall trees. They tell the roots when and how much to elongate, and direct the trunk to expand.

Phosphorus has powers similar to nitrogen. The old Greeks stood in awe and wonder when they saw phosphorus glow with a soft greenish-blue light while steadily heating itself up until it burst into flame. The word phosphorus is a nickname which the Greeks used for Venus, the morning star. It means Bearer of Light. The tendency of this element to kindle spontaneous fire makes it useful on match tips. But phosphorus is far more useful as a growth stimulant in trees. It makes a high-energy substance (ATP) which is concentrated where extra activity is needed, in ripening fruits, in seeds, in the sheath of cells making new wood and bark around the trunk, and in the avid root tips.

Potassium is another virtuoso in tree life. Potassium makes potash, a powerful burning caustic, seemingly untouchable and destructive of wood or leaves. But, strangely, tiny amounts of potassium make wood softer and more flexible. Potassium enters into the pectin of fruits (the basis of jelly), stimulates buds and root tips to greater activity and seems to act as a policeman, protecting the tree's life by neutralizing the poison of sodium.

Of all the violent elements in tree life, none is more exciting than sulfur. Sulfur makes its entrance on the stage when it is released from the earth's crust by volcanic eruptions. Ancient man was astounded and dazzled by sulfur, the stone which burned completely away and left no ash. Its original name was brimstone (burn-stone), and as fire and brimstone it became the symbol of the punitive powers of hell. It was the spirit, the essence, of fire. The celebrated glass bell for making spirit of sulfur was a feature of chemistry laboratories until the eighteenth century.

Modern chemical research discovered that minute quantities of sulfur exert particular powers in sulfa drugs. A century ago it was known that sulfur played a part in human life, according to Charles Dickens in *Nicholas Nickleby*. Mrs. Squeers, matron of a children's home, was wont to give the moppets under her care "substantial doses of brimstone and treacle each morning, partly because if they hadn't something or other in the way of medicine they'd be always ailing and giving a world of trouble, and partly because it spoils their appetites and comes cheaper than breakfast and dinner."

Mixed with charcoal and nitrogen, sulfur makes gunpowder. Fixed in a molecule between hydrogen and oxygen, it makes sulfuric acid whose nauseating odor bespeaks a chemical laboratory. Sulfuric acid exerts its energies in the manufacture of metal alloys, petroleum products, the treatment of textiles and leather. It generates electricity in storage batteries. Such feats of sulfur are better known than the invisible role it plays in the life of a tree that snares this element in its river of sap and combines it with nitrogen to make amino acids and proteins. Thus, the ancient Spirit of Fire is instilled in every living cell of the tree.

These elements, with particular electronic energy, do not act separately: they must influence each other, they must spark in harmony by being mixed together in the living tree.

Magnesium is also drawn up out of the soil and mounts in the river of sap. Its very name comes from magnetic. Mixed with chlorine, magnesium is an exciting element in pyrotechny. It makes incendiary bombs, flashlights, electric fans, and incites electricity in zinc batteries. It gives the bitter flavor and therapeutic punch to epsom salts. In living trees, magnesium is concentrated at the tips of growing stems and roots, where it spurs cells to elongate and divide faster. Also, it performs a curious service by collecting atoms of phosphorus in the sap and transporting them to the sites where proteins are being made—magnesium merely delivers the phosphorus; it does not enter into the protein.

But the crowning achievement of magnesium is the creation of chlorophyll. In this respect, we can hail magnesium dissolved in the currents of the sea and in the water flowing in tree trunks as the element which laid the cornerstone of life—the famous green pigment, chlorophyll, that makes the food for both kingdoms. So potent is magnesium that a *single* atom of it attached to 136 atoms of carbon, hydrogen, oxygen and nitrogen converts them to chlorophyll.

Chemistry, probing the wonder of chlorophyll, stumbled over a fascinating fact that may reveal an evolutionary kinship between trees and human beings. If the single atom of magnesium is detached from the chlorophyll molecule and an atom of iron is put in its place, the same numbers of atoms and their arrangement become a molecule of red blood. Now the iron dissolved in sap delivered to green leaves also plays a part in the creation of chlorophyll. Iron must be present; it must stand by when the magnesium atom is putting together its chlorophyll molecule. Iron, with its atomic power, bosses the job, but without incorporating itself in the chlorophyll. Trees are made *by* but not *of* iron.

We think of iron as a hard metallic substance, but its virtues are extremely subtle. The magnetism that causes it to orient with the magnetic poles was discovered by early mariners who made a compass by piercing a cork with a needle of iron and setting it afloat. Magnetite is another name for iron ore which, according to legend, comes from the name of a Greek shepherd Magnes, who felt his boots come apart when he was leading his sheep over the slopes of Mt. Ida. He is said to have discovered that magnetic iron in the ground pulled the nails out of the soles of his boots.

Roaming bands of gypsies in ancient Greece dazzled people and feathered their nests with the famous Samothracian rings. They had stumbled upon a lodestone (magnetized iron ore, or magnetite) and found that they could make small iron rings dangle from it. The wonder of lodestone is mentioned by classical Greek writers, and in the Bible, where it is written, "The Lord cast down great stones from heaven." Lucretius just before he committed suicide in 51 B.C. wrote: "This stone men wonder at, as it often produces a chain of rings hanging from it, each in turn experiencing the binding power of the stone." Five hundred years later St. Augustine saw a magnetized iron ring pick up another, and wrote, "I was thunderstruck." In ancient days, meteors called thunderbolts heralded dire events. When one survived burning in the atmosphere, it was picked up, put in a temple and worshipped—"the image which fell down from Jupiter."

Thus before atomic electrons were known, iron seemed to possess supernatural powers. It is no less miraculous that iron, as a mere bystander, causes an atom of magnesium and 136 atoms of four other elements to make tree leaves green with chlorophyll.

The elements mentioned so far make a very tiny part of the physical substance of a tree. Their interplay of electronic energy causes carbon, hydrogen and oxygen to build the body of a tree, and then they instill it with life. But one other element, dissolved in sap and borne up the trunk with the others, does supply building material for the magnificent tower.

Calcium is better known as the builder of armor and bones for animals. Before there were trees, calcium combined with carbon in the sea, making shells for snails and oysters, crabs and lobsters. The material was produced for animal life in such abundance through the ages, and was so indestructible, that the shells of dead creatures accumulated as deep sediments that make the vast limestone deposits of our world.

Calcium, however, is not always inert. Combined with oxygen, it creates lime which heats up and steams with hydrogen vapor when water is added and leaves whitewash that hardens at the touch of air. Concrete is mostly calcium and acts the same way. Calcium atoms give extra firmness to many beautiful structures in a tree. The central midrib and network of veins in a leaf are reinforced with calcium. Where the walls of wood cells are pressed against each other, calcium atoms are inserted

between them. Where fresh cell walls are punctured by insects or rup-
tured by a windstorm, calcium atoms arrive on the site to make quick
repairs with a quick-hardening speck of "concrete."

In ways like these, free and fluid elements dissolved in underground
water contribute to the creation and prosperity of beautiful trees. Many
of these elements are abundant and found almost everywhere, others are
very scarce. Yet the great excess of water lifted, far more than is needed
for a tree's own cells, is insurance that even the rarest elements will turn
up sooner or later. The mighty living system which drives roots into hard
ground, splits rocks, thrusts wedges into cracks of cliffs, lifts canopies of
leaves high in the air, and causes a river of sap to flow between the
deepest root and highest twig—operates on such a scale that it can search
out and find all the elements it needs and deliver them to the right place
at the right time.

chapter eight

Leaf Power of the Forest

FOOD in the human menu is hardly recognized as packaged sunlight, but that is exactly what it is. The art of packaging sunlight was originally discovered by plants in the sea, and seaweeds carried the formula for photosynthesis to the water's edge. There they delivered it to ferns and mosses, which in turn bequeathed it to trees.

Growing in the sunlight, trees could make full use of photosynthesis; in fact, their energy factory worked so well that packaged sunlight was not only incorporated into food but into wood, as we have seen. Then wood, in turn, increased the production of packaged sunlight by lifting green needles and leaves high off the ground into more winds, bringing more oxygen and giving more exposure to sunlight. These towering arrangements led to the grand climax of forests.

Leaf-green does not perform photosynthesis in a single operation, as though water and air were suddenly molded together to make food. The combining of air and water requires a chain of swift chemical reactions that have been an utter mystery until recently, when new and unprecedented techniques of study became available.

Visible sunlight is a small sector of the spectrum of radiations that are known as electromagnetic forces. The spectrum also includes TV and radio waves, heat, ultraviolet rays, X-rays, and the deadly gamma rays

99

from atomic explosions. Pure sunlight, whose colors portray the world around us and delight our eyes, is also the electromagnetic force which powers tree leaves.

This light energy has no material substance. Chlorophyll performs life's most majestic feat by trapping the weightless energy in light as it travels at 186,400 miles a second, and incorporates it in material substance. The sunlight energy is stored, as in a kind of storage battery, ready to be released at any later time. The substance of this storage battery packed with energy by chlorophyll is sugar (glucose) which may be reworked the next minute or years later by other living forces to become starch, wood, oils, proteins or even more chlorophyll. Plant sugar (and thereby the other carbohydrates) consists of carbon, hydrogen and oxygen. It is fortunate that these are the three commonest elements of water and air, for otherwise life could never have produced such a spectacular show as a teeming forest.

Trees inherited chlorophyll's recipe from primitive seaweeds. But if it is true that life cannot exist without chlorophyll and the green pigment can only be made in the living cells of plants, how could life have begun?

We can be sure that the earliest life forms found energy that enabled them to live by and function without chlorophyll, without using oxygen to release the energy in sugar. Science certifies that there was no free oxygen in the earth's atmosphere when life began. The air at that time consisted of ammonia and water vapor, nitrogen and carbon dioxide. The oxygen in our present-day atmosphere was put there by living things as a result of photosynthesis. This is confirmed by some peculiar organisms existing today which have persisted since the dawn of life, living as their ancestors did before there was chlorophyll to trap sunlight or oxygen to breathe.

Yeast is one of these peculiar forms of life. It is a microscopic cell without chlorophyll. Instead of multiplying by the usual method of cell division, yeast multiplies by budding—that is, by blowing bubbles with its protoplasm. Yeast colonies are known as a white substance that ferments wine and makes bread rise. These things happen when a colony of yeast plants is getting its energy in a very old-fashioned way: by fermenting sugars and giving off carbon dioxide instead of by using oxygen from the air.

It is true that before chlorophyll there were no carbohydrates like sugar to supply energy. But around the oozes in the estuaries there would have been some raw elemental hydrocarbons which could be fermented for energy. You can see this going on today in stagnant bogs, where still black water bubbles and gives off a foul odor. Certain very ancient microorganisms are buried in the ooze, where they are living cut off from oxygen. They get their energy by fermenting (eating) elemental hydrocarbons,* which gives off hydrogen bubbles smelling of butyric acid, an odor of ancient life processes which is also the smell of rancid butter and human perspiration.

But even if there were no raw hydrocarbons to eat, the iron bacteria show how it is possible to live by eating iron atoms, while the sulfur bacteria demonstrate that sulfur atoms will do. And the remarkable purple bacteria (often they are yellow and green) carry on photosynthesis whether in light or complete darkness. They live on metals without oxygen—shifting at will from one way of getting energy to the other. They are half turned into leaves.

Those microscopic blobs of life that can live on elemental iron, sulfur or natural gas and which breathe no oxygen, have not changed since the beginning of life on earth. They tell us what life on this planet would be like today if chlorophyll had never been invented.

At first glance, a leaf may look as thin as paper; actually it is a spreading one-story factory with ample room between floor and ceiling for sunlight-packaging machinery. The standard leaf ** is designed for utility to present a broad surface to the sunlight. A mature maple tree spreads several hundred thousand leaves with a surface of some 2 thousand square yards (about half an acre) of chlorophyll.

A square yard of leaf surface in full operation packs about a gram of carbohydrate per hour. This may seem to be a small amount; a gram weighs about as much as the common straight pin. But food production of that half acre of chlorophyll mounts with each hour of every day. There are no Sunday and holiday shutdowns. Photosynthesis does not require a bright sunny day, it works even better when the sky is overcast. Operating an average of ten hours a day during June, July and August, each square yard of maple leaf surface packs a pound and a half of carbohydrate. The seasonal production by the leaves of a single maple tree can total 3,630 pounds of packaged sunlight!

* One of these could be methane, CH_4 (natural gas).
** Pine needles are a more primitive form of leaf which does not fit this description, but pine needles have chlorophyll and they package sunlight in the same way that broadleaves do.

If a group consisting of expert mechanical, hydraulic, and chemical engineers, assisted by an avant-garde architect, designed a food factory operated by sunlight, they could not design anything more efficient, or more beautiful than a tree leaf.

The upper side of the leaf is transparent and waxed with cutin that makes it airproof and waterproof. Long cells (palisade cells) filled with chlorophyll dangle like sausages from the ceiling so that sunlight coming through the roof passes through them lengthwise. The palisade cells reach about halfway to the floor, and below them piles of plump, spongy cells are jumbled loosely together with copious air spaces between them. These plump cells are filled with water which seeps out through their walls to be evaporated by the air which circulates among them.

The floor under the spongy cells, the underside of the leaf, is transparent and waxed like the roof except that it is perforated with tiny pores called stomata (little mouths), through which air passes in and out of the leaf. There are more than 100 thousand stomata for each square inch of maple leaf. Each pore has a valve that opens and closes it. Such arrangements for packaging sunlight inside the leaf meet the highest standards of a food-processing factory.

Chlorophyll molecules are lumped together in tiny saucers called chloroplasts, and these green saucers are assembled in lots of 20 to 100 inside each of the palisade cells that hangs from the ceiling. The green saucers are stacked one on top of another in a vertical column that lets rays of sunlight, coming through the top of the leaf, zip through the maximum number of chloroplasts per cell. The act of trapping sunlight energy and fixing it in solid form takes place entirely within the little green saucers. The instant a modicum of light vibrations is packed it is moved out of the cramped quarters in the chloroplasts to make room for more production. The packages of sugar are stored far and near throughout a tree—down in the roots, in buds, under the bark—stockpiled where their energy will be consumed sooner or later.

The means for transporting these packages is at hand. This is the function of the spongy cells, gathered underneath the palisade cells, which are bulging with water. The water that saturates the walls of the spongy cells is evaporated by the air that has entered through the thousands of pores in the floor of the leaf. This water vapor promptly condenses on the outside surfaces of the palisade cells, where it dissolves the packages of sugar which are oozing out. The nourishing fluid then moves through the leaf stem out of the leaf to locations all the way down to the roots of the tree.

The flow of food out of leaves travels in a direction opposite to the flow of sap coming up through the trunk into the leaves. Thus it requires a separate plumbing system. This brings us to a most remarkable feature of a living tree.

We have considered how wood hoists living cells into the sun and air, while keeping them completely submerged in water as in ancient times when all life was in the sea. Wood performs this act superbly but in so doing a problem in reverse logistics has to be met. Carbohydrates made in the leaves must be transported down into the roots and to cells in the bark that build the trunk wider, as well as to the tips of twigs. This problem had to be solved by the first tree that grew on earth in behalf of all the trees of the forests that came after it.

The food-delivery system is so slight a part of the bulk of the tree, and so microscopic, that it was not comprehended until recent years. Botanists were long familiar with the flow of sap through porous wood from the ground to the leaves, and it was taken for granted that carbohydrates made in the leaves somehow also used the wood transportation system. That opening buds in elongating twigs are well supplied with energy was not so mysterious because they are in the same areas where leaves absorb sunlight. However, this does not explain how carbohydrates turn up at distant places, to power trunk expansion and energetic root growth.

Peculiar moist tissue lining the underside of bark was suspected of playing a part in transporting sugar solutions, but for a long time science remained baffled about the mechanics of the operation and there was a vigorous dispute. Articles appeared in scientific journals pointing out why it was technically impossible for the moist inner bark to transport sugar solutions. This layer of cells is microscopic, seemingly too thin (1/100 of an inch thick) to be the sole food transport system for so great an organism as a tree with its vast canopy of leaves. Moreover, those cells between the wood and the bark, observed through a high-power microscope, are seen not to be hollow cells joined end to end to form tubes like the sap cells in wood.

Today's research laboratories have discovered that the moist inner layer of bark called phloem (Greek for bark) is a tree's only food transport system, with peculiar powers for accelerating the flow.

We noted in a previous chapter how wood is formed by living cells taking in water under pressure that stretches them to the proportions of needles. The wood needles are lined end to end, their walls harden by turning woody, their protoplasm disappears, they die, and leave hollow tubes that are firm, fixed structure. By some mysterious genius, the cells in the outside layer of the trunk's wood never die; they form a juicy delicate living fabric that enwraps all the fresh wood of the tree from the crown of the canopy to the deepest roots. This surface veil is 3-ply, each layer only one cell thick.

The middle layer is called cambium from the Latin word *cambiare,* to exchange. This is the site of vigorous chemical activities where electronic forces produce utterly different results on its opposite faces. Wood cells that transport water *into* leaves are produced on the inner surface; the cells that line the bark (phloem) which convey packaged sugar *out of* the leaves are produced on the outer surface. Thus each cambium cell is doing different things at the same time on opposite sides of itself— cambium is an amazing feat of trees.

The thickness of the new wood cambium lays around old wood each year varies with the weather. When heavy winter snows load the ground with water, and rainy weather keeps the trunk well filled with sap all summer, the abundance of water stimulates cambium to produce bigger wood cells and a wider layer of new wood that year; in a dry year the new layer of wood is thinner. As wood layers thicken, the cambium cylinder expands horizontally as new cells with cambium powers are added to enclose the greater girth.

Leaf-dropping in mid-October signals the end of the growing season, and thereafter the cambium performs its off-season job of converting sugar solutions into starch and packing it into wood rays, which we see as silvery ribbons that run horizontally in the grain of wood.

When spring comes again, the cambium starts making new wood, starch stored inside the trunk as wood rays makes energy available throughout the tree for full-scale production of new wood before leaves have unfurled and started packing sunlight. Indeed, starch energy is so great that the first wood cells made in the spring are the plumpest and largest; as the season progresses they gradually become smaller until the late-summer wood cells are the smallest and most compact with the heaviest cell walls. Wood making is suspended in winter, which leaves the wider cells of the following spring against the narrower, tight and darker cells of last fall. This creates the annual wood rings seen on the stump of a tree.

We have seen how virtually the whole life of a tree, regardless of how massive and mighty it looks, is concentrated in a delicate fabric that envelops its exterior surfaces of trunk and twigs just beneath the bark. It would be hard to imagine a more preposterous arrangement than for the delicate living cells to be wrapped around the outer surfaces, exposed to burning sun, freezing wind and rain, and all the assaults of violent weather in the revolving seasons. But corky bark was invented.

Although bark is wrought with dead material, it grows and expands with its tree. Although it is firm and tough, it flexes with the curve of trunk and limb. Although attacked by moisture and decay, it has capacities for resistance and repair. Its foundations are always new and fresh, even on a tree that lives a thousand years.

As a shield of living cells, bark is a remarkable invention. Has it not carried trees through the cataclysms of geologic time? The most famous armor ever produced for land animals was that of the reptiles of the Age of Reptiles, who survived thereby for some 50 million years. Trees have lived on earth eight times longer, and they are still doing pretty well (despite today's attacks on forests by man himself). The thunder lizard grew thirty tons of armor that spelled its doom when the tremendous weight kept it from moving around to feed. On the other hand, a tree does not have to move around, yet it is never overloaded with bark. Bark is light-weight armor, carried by an organism that only has to swing its branches in the wind and carry its leaves high to be well fed.

In manufacturing outer corky bark, the influence of cambium reaches through and beyond the veil of live phloem to pile up on the surface of the trunk a foam of cells that quickly die and become mixed with fatty waxy substances, and filled with air spaces. Each kind of tree concocts its own chemical formula for its bark foam, with combinations of oils, resins, spices and tannin, and sometimes a rubbery fluid called latex.

The bark materials have an appearance that characterizes their special tree. Some trees have thin smooth glossy bark which retains the elasticity of its young foundation so that the surface does not split and crack as the trunk expands. Aspen, birch, young cherry trees and beech have beautiful smooth, often polished, bark. On most trees the cambium piles on more corky bark each year so that some of the outer layer must break off and be cast away to keep the bark armor in proportion to the diameter of the trunk. This procedure gives pines and most of the big hardwoods their rough sculpturing, where bark is bursting apart as underlying layers of new wood push it outward.

When sunlight filters through patterns of veins, leaves resemble stained glass windows.

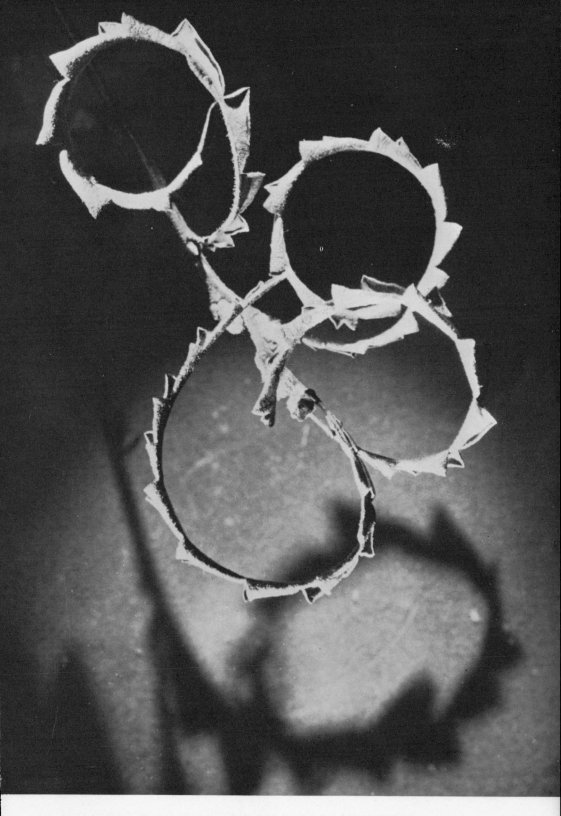

In winter the dry leaves of sweet fern look like whirling gears. This fragrant bush enlivens arid, unfertile spots in the northeast deciduous forest.

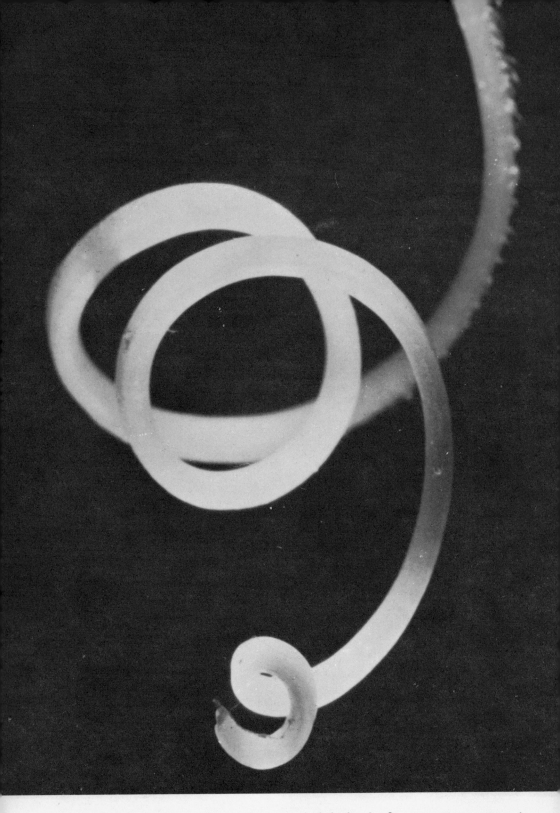

Tendrils of vines reaching in almost musical rhythm for firm supports to grasp and climb on. (Wild cucumber.)

This is no haphazard break-up of bark. Bark sculpturing tells the kind
of tree. Chestnut, oak, sassafras and black locust have the deepest fissures
and the highest ridges. Elm has shallow ridges running lengthwise on
the trunk. On ash, the bark ridges are crisscrossed with diamond shapes.
Red cedar bark is shredded, and shagbark hickory has long tough strips
which break loose and curve out at the bottom while hanging on at the
top. Sycamore's bark is not sculptured; it has a thin, brown outer layer
that falls off in patches, exposing the whiter, elastic bark underneath.
Big-tree sequoia, the old monarch, has such a gigantic trunk, that it can
wear with the greatest of ease bark which is 2 feet thick and so fortified
with chemicals that it is fireproof and rotproof.

Ponder the astounding nature of a forest tree. Its body is built of wood
cells that endure as long as the tree stands—and that may be for centuries. Indeed, to this day, wood cells are standing in their places inside
great trees on our Pacific coast where they were installed before King
David wrote the Psalms and King Solomon built the temple. This body
is wrapped in weatherproof bark, automatically renewed and reinforced
yearly. And between bark and wood is inserted the sheath of living cells,
virtually indestructible by natural hazards, that maintains the whole tree
and makes it grow with well-balanced proportions.

The food transporting system of the tree is as peculiar as its name,
phloem. An astonishing feature is the way this exquisite fabric is created
each year all over the tree at the same time. Phloem appears promptly
when buds start opening in the spring. Last year's phloem is dead; it
dried up and collapsed during the winter. But now, a couple of days of
warm sunlight will unfurl enough leaf surface to put the leaves' food-
making machinery into high gear, and fresh phloem must be ready to
rush energy to all parts of the tree.

Obviously, a complete phloem system cannot be built overnight by
the usual cell-splitting method. But the new food-delivery system does
appear all at once, thanks to the remarkable nature of cambium, the
middle layer of the 3-ply living skin that enwraps the trunk and twigs.
While cells on the inner face of the cambium die as they turn into wood,
and cells on its outer face in the phloem live but a few months while
they are transporting food, the spark of life never goes out in cambium
cells. Even in midwinter, when a tree looks like a corpse quivering in a
blizzard, and the thermometer hovers around zero for weeks on end, its

delicate cambium garment is alive and unharmed. How can this be? Why does a tree not freeze to death?

With the onset of winter a tree performs another chemical feat. It puts a stronger solution of nitrogen and ammonia, a touch of wax or fat into the cambium cells—and into buds which are exposed to the winter air. This makes the cell nuclei larger, toughens them and gives them added resistance. It thickens and gels the protoplasm so that, if it does freeze, its structure will remain intact; it will not crystallize and become brittle. Treated in this way, cambium cells, when thawed out, are alive and ready to go to work where they left off. Let bitter winds pierce the tree and chill it through and through, even freezing the sap in its wood and chilling its protoplasm. The tree is still in business.

Cambium cells, even those in roots deep in the ground, do not begin to grow until the first bud opens. A chemical substance called auxin is made *only* in buds and leaves near the tips of twigs. Auxin, like a Paul Revere, travels by night, awakening cells, summoning them to start growing. The name auxin is well chosen; it is derived from the Greek word for increase (our word auxiliary is derived from it). Auxin seems to explain the deep mystery surrounding the forces that control growth in a tree. Modern chemical skill has deduced the atomic nature of the auxin molecule. It contains the same elements as common carbohydrates, but in auxin they are combined in peculiar proportions; 18 atoms of carbon are arranged in a ring in the center of the molecule, 32 atoms of hydrogen are attached to this ring and there are only a skimpy 5 atoms of oxygen.

Its chemical nature makes auxin a sensitive acid that can migrate in an electrical field. Electrical discharges in energetic cambium are suspected to be the forces that distribute auxin throughout a tree. Auxin always moves in one direction, away from buds and leaves in the highest terminals, where it is created, and down the tree trunk in the phloem to the roots at the other end. Thus auxin concentrates in roots and exerts its greatest influence in elongating them. Since light lessens its power, auxin tends to gather on the shaded side of branches and stems. This stimulates the cells there to grow bigger and to elongate more than those on the sunny side. The imbalance of cell sizes causes a leaf stem or twig to bend and turn toward the light, and thus exposes more leaf surface to more sunlight.

Auxin can be extracted and used as a laboratory chemical which retains its power to quicken growing. When it is applied to cells in a laboratory, they wake up and grow. One molecule of auxin from one little bud is enough to make one little root elongate and start its spring activities in the tree. But when spring really arrives, and with one accord thousands of buds open all over the crown of the tree, an avalanche of auxin is released. In the dark hours this sweeps down the trunk of the tree, and floods the canopy, causing roots and twigs to start elongating, the trunk to expand and the tree to pulse with life. Then the cambium boils with new cells on both its faces and from top to bottom, and a fresh layer of phloem is swiftly created.

In forming a continuous food delivery system, phloem cells elongate, becoming slender needles like wood cells. Instead of sharp points the tips of the needles are cut off, and tiny plates are substituted. These are perforated with perhaps a hundred holes, which gives them the name of sieve plates. The chains of cells are called sieve tubes. The plates are set at steep angles so that the sieve tubes fit together end to end like a carpenter's mortise.

Meanwhile, in the protoplasm of each phloem cell, a bubble has appeared which enlarges and elongates with the growing cell until it fills the cell and the protoplasm is but a thin film lining the cell wall. Welding of cells together at their sieve plates, and the bubble, happen in a flash. This curious delivery mechanism is all at once completed, all new and ready to carry dissolved sugars and auxins throughout the tree.

An ordinary living cell must have a nucleus to stay alive. But there is no nucleus in the film of protoplasm lining the cavities of sieve tubes. They are no longer mixing bowls of life; their protoplasms are not self-contained, flowing round and round within the cells. They are links in a continuous chain of protoplasm, running through millions of sieve tubes, communicating from cell to cell by silvery protoplasmic wires strung through the holes in the plates.

Nevertheless, it is a law of life that protoplasm in a cell must have the service of a nucleus. Where the unique character of a sieve tube rules out a nucleus, a companion cell with a nucleus is supplied to each sieve tube. In some cases there may be two or three companion cells. These are not necessarily fitted to their sieve tubes; they may be longer or shorter. They are only there to lend the services of their nuclei. They simply gather around and offer aid like a boxer's attendants. Companion cells are no particular shape and they are succulent like ordinary living cells, but they have extra large nuclei and they specialize in collecting phosphorus which gives them extra vitality to share with their sieve tubes.

For purposes of being transported through this sieve tube system, carbohydrates that had been stored in various forms—sugars, starch, oil, fats, proteins—are all converted into one kind of sugar (sucrose) and dissolved in water. This fluid sugar moves through the sieve tubes.

The auxins act like little brains. They are not energy; they only push the buttons, throw the switches and dictate where and how the energy is to be exerted. They acquired this talent from other members of the protein family, the enzymes, which direct operations inside cells. Auxins are like traveling enzymes.

Chlorophyll up in the green leaves is another example of tree genius. Scientists have tended to deify protein as the essence of life, but my candidate is chlorophyll. Without it, protein would have for its subjects only some paltry microscopic things which could exist momentarily on meager rations of phosphorus and sulfur. In the glorification of protein, the true greatness of chlorophyll is overlooked. Perhaps this is because chlorophyll is so obvious, and calling it a pigment which makes leaves green and carries on photosynthesis is a satisfying tag. But let us look into it a little deeper.

First, what a laboratory nature gave chlorophyll to work in! We have mentioned the utter beauty and perfection of a leaf: the palisade cells, the spongy cells with generous space between them for air to circulate, the waterproof roof which permits sunlight to pour through, the floor with its perforations through which air and water vapor pass, each controlled by a valve that opens and closes it, the well-fitted plumbing of this laboratory, with pipelines delivering a continuous supply of water from the ground far below, and the remarkable system of living sieve tubes to carry off the packages of sugar so that the leaf laboratory never becomes clogged.

The chlorophyll molecule is not so huge and complicated as the protein molecule. Its framework is a square with four atoms of nitrogen at each corner and one atom of magnesium in the center. An arrangement of 55 carbons, 72 hydrogens, and 5 oxygens linked together surrounds this square and is fastened to it.

Photosynthesis is not performed by a passive leaf hung out in the sunlight. Both the whole leaf and the green chlorophyll in its cells behave in concert for the most successful operation. When light is the best for photosynthesis—not too dim, not too intense—the stem of the leaf turns the blade to present its surface at right angles to the course of the sunlight shooting into it. Too intense sunlight overloads the food factory by using up chlorophyll molecules faster than they can be replaced. Therefore, in very bright sunlight the operation is slowed down by a leaf stem revolving its blade so as to present the narrow edge to incoming light.

The chloroplasts are also co-operating. When the light is just right, they flatten their saucers and take positions at right angles to the light while thronging to the top end of a palisade cell as though competing for a chance to make the most food. By the same token, when the light is either too bright or too dim for business, as at night or when a black thundercloud passes over the sun, the chloroplasts curl up and take time out.

The full operation of packaging sunlight energy in the leaf factory is on a 24-hour schedule. Most of the work is done in darkness, or in daytime without using any sunlight. Sunlight is used only in the first step— to split a molecule of water (H_2O). The radiance of light cuts apart the water's hydrogen and oxygen.

In today's science, light energy is a physical thing that can be measured and played with. It is a unit of electricity, one electron volt called a photon. It takes four electron volts—or four photons—to tear apart the hydrogen and oxygen in one molecule of water. This precisely metered, this finely gaged act, is the fulcrum of life. After the splitting of water, four volts of electricity taken from the light are left attached to the two hydrogen atoms. The oxygen in that molecule of water is thrown away, expelled into the air—and so it is that green leaves put oxygen into our atmosphere.

After the hydrogen is loaded with electricity in this way, photosynthesis can proceed without the services of light so far as this atom of hydrogen is concerned. With its four electron volts it is in a high state of energy. You can think of it as vibrating and madly intent on uniting with a molecule of another element by which, as the chemist says, this hydrogen can be satisfied and calmed down.

The other molecules of sugar (carbon and oxygen) come from air which pervades the leaf—carbon dioxide (CO_2). Arrangements of cells inside a leaf with air spaces between them ensures that air and water are constantly meeting; so our electrified hydrogen from the water promptly merges with carbon dioxide from the air. They proceed to build—by a series of steps spurred along by phosphorus—a full-fledged molecule of carbohydrate, a unit of food containing as many electron volts of energy as four times the number of hydrogen atoms built into it. After light splits the water, it takes about thirty seconds to produce a molecule of sugar or fat. The actual time depends on temperature as this is an ordinary chemical process. It is extremely slow when compared with the speed of the flash of light that splits the H_2O; the dark phase of photosynthesis is much longer than the sunlight phase.

Although the astonishing insights and techniques of present-day science have fairly well analyzed what takes place in a green leaf, man can make sugar glucose in a test tube only by slow stages, laboriously, and with temperatures and chemicals which would quickly destroy a living cell. And the result is only a few insignificant grains of sugar. While the scientist labors for days with his precarious experiment, green leaves outside his window, without the slightest fuss, are making an abundance of sugar within thirty seconds of a flash of light, and at a balmy temperature.

Although it is said that agitated hydrogen quickly finds its carbon dioxide in the air inside the leaf, this is speaking loosely. Only a small fraction of one percent of the air is carbon dioxide. In electronic terms, it is a deep mystery how the four photons of light energy go in search of the right molecule, find it, and are delivered to it with the four volts intact. The act is sure and fast, and unexplained. Thus the green leaf keeps its crucial secret.

There is no dearth of energy pouring into a leaf unfurled in the sunlight. On a fair day the leaves of a forest are exposed to the same intensity of sunlight as desert sand. The surface of the dead metallic sand becomes fiery hot and reflects a blinding glare. What a contrast to the way green leaves handle the violence of radiant energy! Trees equipped with green leaves make land life possible on our planet, not only by ambushing water before it evaporates or flows into the sea, but by quenching excessive sun power while selecting particular energies or wavelengths of light to make food.

Such is the magnitude of the achievement where one square inch of green leaf absorbs one calorie of energy from sunlight per minute.* This may seem to be only a tiny bit of energy, but when you multiply minutes into daylight hours and realize that a single maple tree may spread half an acre of leaf surface with several hundred thousand leaves, the input

---

* One calorie measures the amount of warmth it would take to raise the temperature of about half an ounce of water one degree centigrade.

of energy into the leaf factories of a forest is incalculable. Statistics tell us that all the oxygen in the vastness of our atmosphere is filtered through chlorophyll every 2 thousand years, and that all the carbon dioxide in the air passes through green leaves every 300 years. This spells a power operation by chlorophyll that generates a hundred times more kilowatts of energy a year than all man's hydroelectric plants, coal, gas, fuel oil, and atomic-energy generators combined.

The one calorie per square inch of green leaf is so far from trivial that it presents the leaf food factory with a monstrous problem. Intense light tends to reduce the rate of photosynthesizing. The leaf's food factory operates with maximum efficiency at about one quarter to one half the intensity of full sunlight. This contributes greatly to the success of the whole show, because in moist, temperate climates (where most forests grow) the sky is more often cloudy than clear. The forest is not harmed because leaves pack just as much light energy on a rainy day as when the skies are clear.

We have noted how leaves modify bright sunlight by turning edgewise to it, and how chloroplasts curl up and go off duty when the light is too bright. In addition, the skin (epidermis) of the top surface of a leaf exerts a considerable control over the light which passes through it. Leaves weakly illuminated in the shadows of a forest become almost 100 percent transparent to light, while leaves in very bright light on mountains, deserts, and prairies admit only about 20 percent of the vibrating energy which strikes them.

Leaf skin fends off light by mobilizing pigments and resins, by reflecting more light by means of a shiny surface or by shading the surface with hairs. Invisible high-energy ultraviolet radiation, which gives people at the seashore a vicious sunburn, would destroy delicate chlorophyll if the skin of the leaf did not keep this part of the sun's radiance from entering. The leaf, however, admits all the other wave lengths of the visible sunlight spectrum.

On the other hand, light which enters the leaf is used more efficiently because of the arrangement of the palisade and spongy cells. Light is reflected and refracted backward and forward between the air spaces and cell walls on a zigzag path through a leaf, which makes it course inside the food factory several times longer than a leaf's thickness.

Like an artist who mixes his colors with care and precision and then paints with a very tiny brush, chlorophyll uses particular light vibrations in its work, and less than two percent of the light energy inside a leaf.

To split water, it requires a sharp narrow band of orange and red vibrations and a wide band of blue. When these colors are subtracted from the spectrum by being transformed from light into carbohydrate, the middle of the spectrum where we find green located between blue and orange is left mostly unused, to be discarded by being reflected out of the leaf. This is why a leaf is green. It is a throwing away of the part of the spectrum that is not used in photosynthesis.

One more astonishing feature of the leaf's operation remains to be told. While ultraviolet radiation was fortunately barred from entering the leaf, infrared radiation at the other end of the spectrum fortunately was not. The long-wave vibrations of infrared are so weak in energy that this quality of light cannot be used for splitting water molecules, and chlorophyll does not absorb it. But infrared is easily transformed into heat, and when this invisible red light circulates in the air spaces between the cells it raises the temperature of the whole interior of the leaf. This speeds up the chemical processes of photosynthesis in the same way that life processes are quickened in warm-blooded birds and mammals. The temperature inside a photosynthesizing leaf may be 50 degrees higher than the temperature of the outside air. Indeed, unless checked, the inside of a leaf could become unbearably hot by trapping infrared rays—as everyone knows who gets into a car that has been standing tightly closed in the sun. But the wonderful checks and balances of leaf mechanics, prevents overheating.

Heat evaporates water, and water vapor dissipates the heat in the air, reducing the temperature. There is plenty of water oozing out of the spongy cells, ready to be evaporated by the infrared rays in a leaf, and the vapor escapes into the outer air through perforations in the under-surface of the leaf. This keeps temperatures inside the food factory within bounds. When a day is extra bright and clear and the sun stands at zenith, flooding a forest with infrared vibrations, accelerated vaporizing inside the leaves pulls up from the ground greater amounts of water. This makes the sap flow faster up the trunks of the trees, and their leaves gush invisible water vapor into the air.

One question is still unanswered. How can a tree without a pump force tons of water to flow upward against gravity? The pipelines in the wood are microscopically slender so the column of water is drawn into practically weightless threads, although continuous from roots to leaves. The water molecules on the surface of a drop of water strongly cohere, and in extremely slender threads of water all molecules are surface. Water evaporating in the leaves sets up a tension in the threads of water which is exerted all the way down to the roots. The tensile strength of sap— its ability to stretch the thread without breaking it—has been found to be as great as 2,250 pounds to the square inch. This is 150 times greater than the pressure of the atmosphere. It is enough to lift sap many times higher than the tallest trees—merely by the gentle tug of evaporation at the top.

chapter nine

Genius of the Forest, P-730

THE first non-cone-bearing forests were tropical and composed of broadleaf, evergreen trees. We can see some of them in our deciduous forest today. They are mountain laurel, holly, rhododendron and magnolia. With their spectacular flowers, these are some of the most beautiful features of our deciduous forest. Their green foliage catches a spotlight in the forest among the stark silhouettes of other hardwood trees in winter. They are unusual in the way they retained the evergreen nature of their ancient ancestors in tropical hardwood forests, even during bitter winters.

We might expect to find more cone-bearing needle trees mixed with our deciduous hardwoods, instead of herded by themselves in more or less pure stands. Only a few of the needle trees, through the fortunes of evolution, became at home in the deciduous forest—hemlock, white pine and junipers (including red cedar, botanically a juniper).

Leaf-dropping was not an innovation of the deciduous forest. All conifers drop their needles—all pines, spruces, firs, hemlocks, junipers and cedars—as is seen in the red carpets of fallen needles under these trees. All broadleaf evergreen trees also drop their leaves. A leaf, whether it is in the form of a needle or a blade, is not part of the permanent structure of a tree. It is a tender organ that must be frequently replaced. However, the heavily waxed, leathery leaves of the broadleaf evergreens are able to protect their chlorophyll cells in winter as well as the indurate resinous needles of conifer trees. So, all evergreens disregard the season and replace their leaves a few at a time. Rust-colored dead needles are often seen on pine trees, or fluttering to the ground. But evergreen trees retain enough needles on their branches all the time to make green foliage the year round.

The needle trees are time-honored patriarchs with ancestors dating to the Age of Reptiles. Their reproductive organs are tough cones, able to pollinate by gravity, and in dry chill wind. Their seeds lie naked on wooden, long-lasting cone scales, where they are seasoned to withstand the caprices of weather—in contrast to the seeds in flowers with succulent evanescent petals and parts. Needles twang and quiver in high winds and —like all parts of the conifer tree—are waxed and insulated by resin that gives them fine protection against drying.

Due to their different natures, we can imagine that when the broadleaf forests originally appeared on earth they did so in moister milder climates, while the needle trees were migrating into drier, sandy ground, and more windswept, cooler, higher locations. When an Ice Age mounted, the conifers could take it. Their forests could spread farther north than the broadleaf evergreens whose tender-skinned, pulpy leaves shrivelled in cold, drying winds.

This situation called forth the deciduous forest.

Imagine it happening. The needle trees have moved off across the horizon. The broadleaf trees are held back in warmer wetter places, although it is their nature to spread vigorously. Their seeds cast farther away, a bit nearer to the colder weather, and sprout, but their seedlings die when their leaves fail to operate in the unaccustomed cold.

In this context, the evolution of the deciduous forest would be a natural, inevitable outcome when some of those seedlings, instead of dying, developed winter buds which could wait for weeks or months, until the weather moderated, to sprout again. Where this occurred the ground would become more fertile under the fallen leaves. Seeds would be protected and could join the cycle of the winter buds, waiting comfortably to sprout when the weather moderated, as it always did. Moreover, those seeds sleeping under the moist and comparatively warm leaf cover, would find their situation highly nourishing and stimulating. The mineral sands became humus after a few years of fallen leaves.

The rise of the deciduous forest must have occurred with great rapidity; for a major turn of evolution its speed would have been unprecedented.

The needle-cone forests had grown for 100 million years; they were sluggish, stolid and uncreative compared to the energetic and flexible deciduous forest that someday would generate our kind of world.

A deciduous forest, particularly one with the splendor of the forest which awaited our coming between the Atlantic coast and the Mississippi River, is far greater than the sum of its deciduous trees. Deciduousness was a dynamic property that induced resonance in the forest.

Resonance results when small impulses are echoed and amplified to larger and stronger impulses. A loudspeaker amplifier is a good example. The feeble sound of a vibrating string produces a full rich note when it is echoed by the sounding board of a piano. When the pioneer deciduous forest cast off its leaves all at the same time in the autumn instead of a few at a time around the year, this was, at first, a minor adjustment. But the life processes of the forest acquired resonance from the cycle of the seasons. With leaves, buds, flowers, fruits, berries, seeds and fresh twigs in the rhythm of the seasons, animal life, also prodded by weather, joined the mighty resonance of the deciduous forest. Evaporation of water from the tree ceased when the leaves fell. Enzymes made cork with which to plug the pipe ends on the twigs where the leaves had been attached. The sap stopped flowing, the body of the tree was sealed up.

The violence of this cessation was so great that it was reflected throughout the economy of the tree. The buds for both flowers and leaves, which had been inherited from evergreen ancestors in the tropics, could not open without sap. They were immobilized, became dormant, while more enzymes worked on their predicament by surrounding their infantile flowers and leaves with scales weatherproofed by wax, resin or fur. Seeds, which had sprouted at any time of the year in evergreen ages, whenever conditions permitted, now found that conditions permitted them to sprout only in step with the spring. A particular enzyme, labeled P-730, turned up in seeds and synchronized their sprouting with the best conditions.

This recently detected auxin, P-730, is a bluish speck of protein that stimulates the reproductive organs of forest trees and bushes. A tree has no brain stem to arouse emotions, but these astonishing blue specks perform the function of emotions with aplomb. They excite stamens and pistils to erupt from their buds—and, participate in the whole cycle of reproduction. Months later, they will cause embryos to break out of their seeds and sprout.

In deciduous forest trees, leaves and flowers are usually in separate buds, with the leaf bud below the flower bud on a twig. P-730 originates in a new-born leaf on the day it catches a ray of sunlight and starts to unfurl. It has not yet turned green with chlorophyll, but it is colored with yellow or red pigments, hairy and sparkling with droplets that act like tiny lenses focusing light rays in its interior. There, among those glittering pigments, the peculiar protein molecule is created.

So recently has P-730 and its wonderful influence been discovered that words have not yet been found to describe it precisely. Scientists variously call it an enzyme, a plant hormone and a phytochrome (a unit of plant color). They refer to its actions as though a tree has senses. P-730 "perceives," and "measures time." This "intelligent" chemical emerges from its pigment cells in the leaf, travels down the leaf stem, then up the twig and enters the nearest flower bud. Since leaf and flower buds are on the same twig this is a local jaunt compared to the fabulous voyages of auxins that go from top to bottom of tall trees. The average distance is four inches, and P-730 leisurely takes around 24 hours for the trip. The P-730's enter the dormant organs—the male stamens and female pistils (sometimes combined in the same flower)—and arouse them.

Here among forest trees is an uncanny parallel to hormones made in the pituitary gland of the human skull which travel unerringly to gonads to stimulate the production of sperm, and to release an ovum every lunar month. Phytochromes in trees, however, are not tied to the 28-day moon cycle but to the annual cycle of the seasons—that is, a sun-water-temperature cycle. This brings us to the amazing ability of P-730.

Everybody knows the fickleness of weather, particularly in the zone of the American deciduous forest. The thermometer may go above 50 in midwinter, and within a few hours drop close to zero. One day can be fair and sunny; on the next a blizzard can rage. If the flower buds of trees were sprung by every mild spell in winter, their succulent tender parts would be frozen on the first cold night. The magnificent deciduous forest would never have survived the hazards of the Ice Age, and life here in America would have been altogether different.

But P-730 has an internal clock by which it measures the hours and minutes the sun is below the horizon each 24 hours. As nights grow shorter and days longer, while winter fades, a time comes (in March in our southern states, in April farther north) when shortening hours of darkness trigger the earliest spring flowers. These are willow and hazelnut, and on the same timetable are skunk cabbage and false hellebore, which bloom when patches of snow still linger in shady places. The following week, with nights about 15 minutes shorter, poplars suddenly

Canoe birch (also called paper birch) with snow white bark is a vivid exclamation point in the winter woods.

Sycamore dates from the Age of Reptiles. Its ancient style of bark is nonelastic. The tree "bursts its breeches" when the trunk expands.

Giant white pine is like a ghost from the great virgin forest which the first settlers in New England saw.

dangle their catkin flowers, shadblow makes a white mist and marsh marigolds flare overnight.

The P-730's seem to know what their respective flowers can stand. Some resist frosty nights better than others. And so the spring procession of flowering is in full stride high in the tree canopies and on the forest floor. Thus, we see willow, hazelnut, shadblow, poplar, red maple, elm, sugar maple, ash, birch, walnut, hickory sycamore, oak, beech, locust, tulip tree, basswood—flowering roughly in that order from March to June.

Since P-730 is strict about the length of each night, which varies with every mile north or south, the actual date of opening depends on latitude. An oak in Maine will bloom several weeks later than an oak in Virginia. Willows will be flowering in northern Minnesota when dogwood blooms in Tennessee. The time perception of P-730 insures the success of reproduction in the forest mile by mile as spring creeps northward.

The ability of P-730 to conjure up perceptive strategies in darkness is dramatized by its control of seed sprouting of forest trees. Every seed contains an embryo, a miniature of its parent tree, with a thread for a root, a minute stem for a trunk and two tiny leaves. This is buried in a wad of starch which nourishes it and packaged in a waterproof, airproof seed coat. This elaborate item, conceived in the spring, is perfected during the summer. After about six months, deciduous forest trees release their seeds which go whirling off in the wind if they have wings like maple, ash and elm seeds, or fall and roll across the ground if they are acorns and nuts or heavy fruits.

This happens in the fall, on the threshold of winter. The embryos are complete but they are tiny and delicate. If, soon after falling to the ground, the seed coat should split and the embryo emerge from its protecting womb into raw dark days of late fall, its chance for survival would be slight. So P-730 withholds the exit permit. The embryo is held in thrall by darkness. With some interesting exceptions, most embryos of deciduous forest trees must dwell in darkness for months before their seeds germinate—generally long enough to bridge the winter.

Opaque fruit skins, hard nut shells, black leathery pods as on locust and Kentucky coffee trees and heavy husks are good accessories. It is just as dark inside a walnut husk as it is underground. The ripening of fruits, pods, husks of nuts and berries is paced with the required dark period. When their minimum time of darkness has elapsed, the prison walls disintegrate and they are released with their P-730's cocked and ready for sprouting.

White oak is a conspicuous exception. Its acorn is a long oval, mahogany brown, polished—a handsome acorn, worthy to be the emblem of the sovereign tree of the American deciduous forest. But one seldom sees this acorn, although the forest floor is strewn with acorns of other oaks. That fine shell of the white oak acorn is not as indurate as it looks. It is thin and brittle and usually cracks when it drops to the ground. The darkness period of white oak's embryo is so short that it is completed when acorns are shed in early fall. You can find white oak acorns sprouting in November in the open air on top of the leaf carpet. This tree was saved for the forest by the squirrels! We shall return to them.

The average periods of darkness for conditioning the seeds of outstanding deciduous trees are: 2 months for sycamore, 3 months for maple, ash, beech, birch, elm, black gum, tulip tree and most oak acorns other than white oak, and 4 months for hickory, walnut, and dogwood. These periods of darkness are long enough to insure against sprouting in Indian summer weather, which would doom them to death in the winter. They are short enough to insure that various species of trees have an equal chance to germinate as soon as winter is over.

Poplars and willows play the game differently. Seeds come off these fast-growing trees in summer, all primed and ready to grow. They will germinate immediately, if conditions are favorable, for poplar and willow seeds can retain their ability to germinate for only a few days. Moreover, their throngs are prevented from crowding out other species by a special provision—their leaf food factories require extra-bright light. They cannot live in the dim forest glades where the seedlings of other trees prosper. This has prevented the aggressive poplars and willows from invading the shadowy depths among the time-honored hardwoods. The role of poplars is to pioneer in open places after a burn or windfall, and on hillsides with good exposure to the sky. The places allotted to willows are the well-lighted, well-watered borders of lakes and rivers and marshes.

The darkness which makes the embryos of seeds potent is not a photoperiod. Seeds do not sprout automatically when their embryos have been treated to a particular length of darkness. The dark period of seeds is a minimum, after which their P-730's will open them according to circumstances. Otherwise too many seedlings would struggle to grow in one spring season and strangle each other. If the blizzard of seeds which shower from one big elm tree sprouted in one season, they could upset the balance of that forest. Seeds may continue in the dark, utterly inert, indefinitely—and without loss of vitality. Their embryos, with the P-730's on hand to make them grow,* will stand by while weeks lengthen into months, months into years.

The timelessness of seeds is one of the startling facts of life. Here are little offspring which have a charmed life—each beautifully packaged with a personal food store, a modicum of moisture and a negligible bit of oxygen. Many seeds can sprout after waiting 10, 20 or even 75 years.

The old fable about germinating grain seeds exhumed from the coffins of Egyptian mummies has been investigated and found to be false, but compared to other kinds of life, embryos in seeds have a touch of eternity. The longest verified record is that of lotus seeds dug up from a dried lake bed in Manchuria which germinated after lying in darkness for 1,040 years (according to the radio-carbon dating method used by geologists).

Darkness-locked seeds germinate when light reaches them. The length of the light period, and the intensity of light, do not matter. But the P-730's which spark the germination of seeds must have a touch of a particular band of red light from the sun's spectrum. It may be dim and quick. In an experiment, dormant seeds kept in utter darkness were triggered by a small hand flashlight, and by a 50-watt lamp more than 3 feet away which were turned on and off as fast as possible.

Dramatic evidence of seeds long held in darkness awakening when struck by light is seen when a field is ploughed after standing idle for years; a tremendous crop of weeds from the past appears. Famous are the flowers and trees that sprang up from seeds unearthed among the ruins of bombed London!

In the wild forest, the dim red light needed to germinate seeds keeps things in balance. During the summer and fall a suffocating shower of seeds descends upon the leaf carpet, and only a tiny percentage of these should be allowed to sprout. Of course birds and rodents go over the carpet cleaning up seeds, but they do not make a clean sweep; they only reduce the number to manageable quantities.

During the winter, rain and melting snow cause many seeds to percolate in dark recesses under the leaves where, without the flash of light to spark them, they succumb to the bacteria of decay. The stipulation

* This is not technically accurate because P-730 has a twin, named P-660, which is inert and does the standing by. P-660 turns into P-730 at the moment of action.

that P-730 must have a flash of red light to make seeds sprout prevents a population explosion and provides good fertilizing.

The seeds of elm, ash, sycamore, maple and sweet gum, have wings and protuberances which keep them on top of the leaf carpet. These are some of the more desirable trees for forest maintenance. Moreover, prickly seed-coat protruberances make such seeds less appealing to birds and rodents. So, a goodly number of this kind of seed are left on top of the leaf carpet to be touched by the first beams of sunlight that slant among the tree trunks after the snow melts. Some of these may have slipped under the top layer of leaves—but the triggering light is a unique red ray that can pass through a dead leaf.

This brings us to the strange career of walnuts, hickory nuts, beech nuts, hazel nuts and acorns. They are too big for the bird-rodent vacuum cleaner, and too big to percolate below the leaves. It would seem that nuts, being in full view on the ground, would have no problem being triggered by light in the spring. But it happens that they do have that problem as a result of special arrangements for getting them into the ground. Squirrels carry them off and bury them before they have completed their period of dark conditioning. Squirrels are so provident that they hoard more than they need, leaving nuts well planted for the economy of the forest. But what about light to inspire their P-730's? How does the forest get its viceroys of walnut, hickory and oak trees to sprout from their buried seeds?

P-730, which is the forest's sense of dark and light, can act in an opposite manner by opening flowers and leaves in the light, and extending roots in the dark. By the same facility for reversing action, it can make big seeds buried by animals germinate without any light at all.

It is remarkable that big seeds buried by animals dispense with the red light trigger. The forest has nut trees only because P-730 can distinguish between little, haphazard, wind-blown seeds, and heavy nuts buried by squirrels. Nuts and acorns, after completing their dark conditioning, need only wait for the ground around them to thaw and for moisture to soften their coats. This applies as well to the exceptional white-oak acorns, which are ready to sprout as soon as they leave their trees. The squirrels usually whisk them away before their germination is visible on the outside—and little white shoots and roots emerge in the squirrels' storage places.

Thus, by the ordinary invention of P-730, the forest, mainstay of land life, had acquired—after 350 million years of infinitely slow evolution—astounding new dimensions.

The deciduous forest now had a dimension of *time*. The life of the forest fluctuated with each passing year, while its predecessors had been virtually timeless. The evolution of the trees and everything with them in the ancient needle forests had flattened out. Evolution in seasonless forests was horizontal through 50 million years of the Devonian, 70 million years of the Coal Age, 50 million years of the Permian, 100 million years of the Age of Reptiles and 30 million years of the Lower Cretaceous—until the first broadleaf forests were simmering in the tropics.

The dimension of time lies in the polarities of spring-fall, summer-winter—life-death, go-stop, positive-negative. Every vital phenomenon pulses like a heart with action-rest periods. Schopenhauer said, "Polarity, the sundering of a force into two opposed activities striving after reunion is a fundamental of almost all the phenomena of nature, from the magnet and the crystal to man." The dimension of time in the seasonal rhythm was the most vital and important new dimension of the forest.

Another new dimension was *color*. Dark tones had predominated in the needle-cone forests—dark-green foliage, dark-brown needles, black tree trunks and dark shadows on the forest floor. But now the deciduous forest flared with light-green foliage, sunlight and colorful spring flowers on the forest floor. There was the green, red and white bark of aspen, cherry, and birch; the silvery bark of beech, the mottled white and yellow bark of sycamore, bright red and blue berries and the flaming yellows, reds, and oranges of autumn foliage. The tropical ancestral forest had large, slow moving and highly colored birds. The north temperate, deciduous forest evolved scintillas of color with quick, darting little birds—cardinal, bluebird, blue jay, goldfinch, yellow flicker, red-headed woodpecker, purple martin, red-wing blackbird, red-breasted nuthatch, robin, wood thrush, bobolink, crossbill, and "a billion" warblers.

There was also the new dimension of *numbers*. Not only the birds but all other forms of life were multiplied in the deciduous forest. Instead of trees of only standard sizes, there were now big trees and little trees, bushes, herbs, big animals and little animals, myriads of insects and vast mysterious populations of soil animals. The place teemed with life.

The teeming life bestowed on the forest its paramount and most dramatic new dimension. The *pyramid of life* was enormously broadened and heightened in the deciduous forest. The foundations of the pyramid are installed in the ground when energy from the sun is trapped in the tree tops and flows into an accumulation of fallen debris consisting of leaves, wood of dead trees, seeds, insects, bud scales, excreta, dead birds, animals and flowers. Every living thing in the forest sooner or later contributes its share of organic energy that descends into the soil.

The base of the living pyramid is all plant life (including trees) which have their roots in the soil. The next level above the plants consists of insects and their larvae—millipedes, centipedes, spiders, mites. Above this is the level of birds and little rodents like mice, gophers, shrews and chipmunks which eat insects. Next above are bigger rodents and smaller mammals such as squirrels and rabbits. Each higher level has fewer numbers and larger bodies than the level below. Just below the peak of this forest pyramid of life are the bobcats, beavers and woodchucks, and at the peak the largest carnivores—bear, wolf, panther, deer. The species in each layer depends on the one below for food and often for other services, and furnishes these necessities of life to the layer above.

There are crossovers and short cuts, such as beavers feeding on trees, squirrels and chipmunks on nuts, deer browsing on twigs. The outline of the restless pyramid is indistinct and flexing, and held together by a tangle of food chains—but it adds up to the most highly successful and diverse system of life on this planet.

chapter ten

The Forest Floor

TALL tree trunks mount out of the ground with the vertical thrust of space rockets. At the base of some trunks, especially on rocky hill sides where the soil has been washed away from the crown of the roots, their contortions depict the Laocoön struggle of tree roots tackling the ground.

Where the forest floor is mottled with sunlight on a spring day, countless tiny flowers are scattered like confetti—trailing arbutus, violet, spring beauty, windflower, starflower, bloodroot, bishop's-cap, and Clinton lily. Brightly colored, delicate, exquisite, they are in utter contrast to the dark, silent soil from which they sprang.

Where patches of sunlight are larger in open forest glades, midspring flowers unwind gracefully from the ground—triangular trillium, fanciful lady's-slipper, jack-in-the-pulpit, wild ginger, Dutchman's-breeches, bleeding-heart, wild columbine. After them come the tall bushes—shadblow, snowberry, elderberry, wild plum, choke cherry—sucking up some essence of the soil that makes them flutter with fresh green leaves and flare with flowers.

Beneath and among these celebrities are ferns, mosses and lichens. An exquisite live thing projects from every square inch of soil surface, all adding up to an immense conclave of vigorous life, pouring and pushing out of the forest floor.

How does "dirt" beget such a pageant, create such beauty? That was
a weighty question throughout 2 thousand years of human history, from
Aristotle to Pasteur, until the latter discovered the bacteria of decay. It
had got all involved with a fundamental belief in spontaneous generation.
The subject was eloquently summed up by Alexander Ross in the seven-
teenth century:

> Who shall doubt whether in cheese and timber, worms are generated; or
> if beetles and wasps in dow's dung; or if butterflies, locusts, grasshoppers,
> snails, eels and such like be procreated of putrified matter. To question
> this is to question reason, sense, experience. If one doubts this, let him
> go to Egypt, and there he will find the fields swarming with mice, begot
> of the mud of Nylus, to the great calamity of the inhabitants.

In this century, the role of the bacteria of decay in making nitrogen
available to forest life has been ferreted out in research laboratories. Before that, earthworms dug by little boys to bait their fishhooks became
famous when Darwin said he doubted that "there are any other animals
which have played such an important part in the history of the world."
But the soil had still kept its deepest secrets.

Today, forest soil is one of the most exciting investigations of science.
The breakthrough into the profound inner spaces of the soil came with
the invention of two marvelous instruments. The electron microscope
offers forty times more magnification than the ordinary microscope, and
the autoradiograph can actually photograph molecules of soil elements
by tagging them with radioactive atoms which they carry like little
lanterns.

Previously the concept of soil under forest trees was that of an in-
coherent mixture of pulverized rock and decaying debris, compressed
into a firm and fertile anchorage for roots. Little animals were seen to
burrow, earthworms to tunnel and work the ground, but a realization
of the magnificence of organization and tremendous activity of the forest
soil awaited the electron microscope.

Forest soil has been revealed as a massive system of life with creative
impulses that mobilize its powers in such a way as to enable forest trees
to overcome all obstacles and rise through the leaf mold. Mature forest
soil consists of a series of layers, each containing limitless galleries which
teem with energetic inhabitants that are perpetually at war. So weird are
the tremendous realms under the forest floor, so fantastic are the beings

which live there, that the sight of their worlds is comparable to getting a close look at a distant planet hitherto but dimly seen.

For a brief time each year, just after the leaves have fallen, the leaf carpet is the most conspicuous feature of the deciduous forest. When the sun is shining on an Indian summer day, the whole forest glows with a golden light unique among the many spectacular color effects of nature. Then a walk in the woods satisfies a hunger for cleanliness and freshness. The place feels tidied up. It is reposeful and hospitable. Trees and bushes go unheeded; the wild flowers and birds are gone. The brown, red and gold carpet is gloriously beautiful.

The crunch and quiver of the ground underfoot, the swish of leaves around the ankles, the earthy fragrance, make the forest peculiarly sensuous and personal. Leaves on the trees had been far away and out of reach, blended in the green clouds of the forest canopy. But now, looking down at the details of the fresh carpet, the outlines of individual leaves attract the eye. No artist could draw more glamorous points, curves, waves and angles. Many of the leaf outlines are damaged by insects or broken, but the intrinsic symmetry of every leaf is revealed in each fragment. At this time of year, people are tempted to collect leaves, drawn by their beautiful colors and designs. They stare down at the forest floor, searching for rare forms, as fascinated as the collectors of colorful stones and shells on a sea beach. But unlike the treasures of the beachcomber, those of the leaf collector in October are everywhere.

The down fall of leaves in deciduous woodland is estimated to average two tons an acre every year, and leaves contribute most of the bulk of the organic debris which accumulates on the forest floor. The annual tonnage of leaves which laid the foundations of this superb American forest was much greater from the tall trees of the virgin wilderness than from the troubled trees of our time.

Yet the weight of fallen leaves is only a fraction of that of green leaves whose content is 90 percent water. The solid residue of the leaves that drop from deciduous trees in October is a dry skeleton with a structure of exquisite delicacy, consisting of a network of hollow tubes and a tissue of delicate cell wells from which all protoplasm has vanished.

Most of the leaf skeletons on the forest floor are whole, despite their fall out of high canopies, and some were torn from their twigs, hurled against trunks and branches, and whipped by winds. Many have lain under damp snow for months during the past winter, or have been soaking for a year or two in shallow depressions. Why don't they deteriorate? Why are so many leaves of the forest carpet intact? Evidently they possess a peculiar durability under conditions of soaking and freezing, searing winds and scorching sun and injurious radiation. People driving on a highway in October see leaves driven by the wind perform a furious ballet across the concrete. They tumble, collide, swirl on their points, turn cartwheels. Yet who has ever seen leaves broken by this hurly-burly? Lightness, wiriness and resilience characterize the ballet dancers.

Leaf skeletons designed to house the meticulous food factory are located at the receiving end of a steady stream of the most vital elements —hydrogen, carbon, oxygen, nitrogen, magnesium, phosphorus, sulfur. The leaf skeleton was once mostly woody, but as time went on the proportion of lignin, with a high concentration of carbon, increased. Also minerals and salts—silica, iron, manganese, copper, zinc, boron and nickel—accumulated in the leaf skeleton. These minerals are more indissoluble than the calcium of animal bones. Indeed, X-ray diffraction studies of a fallen leaf catch the glint of prisms. The ghost which masquerades as a leaf on the forest carpet is the burnt-out skeleton of the green food factory of summer.

If leaves at the end of their food-making season shriveled and shrank and disappeared into thin air or, falling to the forest floor, deliquesced and disappeared into the ground on the first rainy day, the whole character of the forest and its wildlife would be different. It is staggering to imagine how that would have altered the course of evolution.

Leaves of deciduous trees come in all shapes and sizes. They have lobes and sinuses. Their edges are irregular, with sawteeth, waves, rolling angles and curves, making the surface of the forest carpet as disparate and loose as a pile of jackstraws. Leaves exposed briefly to dry air curl and make channels for raindrops. The forest floor collects rain and holds it better than open water, because there is far less evaporation.

The openings between leaves invite multitudes of tiny animals to enter and live in paradise. These smallest of the visible soil animals, are known officially as *meiofauna* (little animal life). Their vigorous and prosperous communities include: gnats, mites, ants, ticks, maggots, springtails, thrips, spiders, earwigs, mealy bugs, millipedes, centipedes, sow bugs, and tardigrades.

For these, the wide arches and open doors among the fallen leaves lead into the State of Euphoria where the atmosphere is deliciously heavy with carbon dioxide and moisture, and warmed by a deep red glow. In warm, damp, dim corridors and caverns grow generous crops of fungi and algae, whose shadowy estates are well stocked with game for the meat-eaters—baby earthworms and slugs, and succulent larvae of moths, flies and beetles.

The meiofauna of the leaf carpet enjoy the greatest degree of well-being and security to be found in any habitat of the forest. Bitter cold poses no threat to them because in the latitude of the deciduous forest the season of freezing temperatures is transitory. After leaf-fall and before the snow comes, radiation reaching the forest floor is mostly long, red warmth-bearing rays of sunlight. The warmth is captured and held by the porous structure of the leaf skeletons. In winter, the undersides of leaves covered by snow are usually damp and unfrozen. In periods of severe cold many members of the meiofauna communities take a good nap. It is a common sight, for example, to see sow bugs coiled into tight spirals as hard as pebbles, practically impervious to cold.

By the same token, spring comes early to the estates in the fallen leaves. The sun-irradiated leaf litter warms instantly when the snow vanishes. This is why early spring flowers bloom on the forest floor even while patches of snow are about, perhaps weeks before tree buds open, high up in the colder air.

Flooding from heavy rain or melting snow would seem to pose an horrendous threat to the meiofauna. But here again the texture of the forest carpet offers ample security. In a mature undisturbed forest the branch-woven baskets of tree canopies break the force of violent downpours; leaves that are interlocked in the carpet are seldom torn apart and borne off in a rush of water. A healthy forest, well-wrought by nature, is hardly ever invaded by seething floods. Moreover, water reaching the forest floor in drops and trickles does not fill all the spaces among the fallen leaves. Even in the worst deluge, bubbles are trapped everywhere, and air-filled capillaries around roots hold more than enough oxygen to keep meiofauna alive until the flood subsides.

However, an awful calamity frequently visits the provinces of the meiofauna. It is the earthworm. Although earthworms are honored allies of the human race, for the smaller meiofauna in the corridors of the leaf litter, coming face to face with an earthworm's slimy snout is like being caught in a tunnel before an approaching locomotive. Millipedes and centipedes can take to their many heels and rush topside, but springtails (one of the most dominant of these populations) cannot spring their tails in cramped quarters, and most of the other meiofauna are torpid. But the earthworm menace is mitigated by the fact that it is seasonal; the worms peak in spring and fall. Also they are fairly localized because they prefer certain kinds of leaves and become segregated under particular trees. Large-tooth aspen (a poplar), white ash, basswood, tulip tree and hickory are first choice. Maple and white oak leaves are tolerable. Forest areas carpeted by leaves of black oak, northern red oak, beech, yellow birch and conifers are spurned by earthworms. They hate acid soil.

Sometimes, in the dimensions of the forest and usually only in isolated places, burrowing mammals such as moles, shrews and woodchucks create awful earthquakes in the meiofauna provinces.

The mole that tunnels the forest floor, called hairy-tailed mole, is first cousin to the golf links or lawn mole. All moles are tireless, voracious insect-devourers. In pursuit of insects they are amazing digging machines. They measure eight inches long, stand two inches at the shoulder, and weigh only four ounces.

Feasting on nutritious teeming meiofauna has shaped the mole like a fat pig, but this is not obesity. It is bulging muscle that operates the forefeet shovels and inflates the body for pushing and compressing the earth. A mole can drive through ground at the rate of fifteen feet an hour. Spending all its life in the faint light under the shadowy floor of a forest has made its eyeballs degenerate, and the lids have grown over them, closing them to mere slits. A mole's blindness is offset by extraordinarily keen senses of touch and smell focused in the tip of its sharp nose. Somehow this equipment also serves as a compass, giving it a sense of direction. Mole tunnels go places; they do not circle like people lost in a forest. Moles navigate by their noses over ridges and across ravines, detouring rocks without breaking through the top of the tunnel or varying the thickness of the tunnel roof.

What happens when an earthworm looms up in front of a mole which is snuffing meiofauna? The mole sucks in the earthworm like slippery spaghetti, holding it with its forefeet, while cleaning off the dirt and straightening out the kinks.

The shrew is a cousin of the mole with slightly better eyesight. It occasionally hunts in the daylight on the forest leaf carpet, yet few people have ever seen a shrew. This is the smallest mammal in the American forest wilderness—three inches long, an inch at the shoulder, and weighing less than an ounce. Victor H. Cahalane describes the shrew as the most high-strung of all our animals: "Every movement it makes is quick and jerky. First a little dash forward, then a quick turn and a lunge at right angles. When fighting it fills the air with continuous high-pitched squeaks. Its feints and passes are almost too swift for the human eye to follow."

The shrew compensates for its small size with wicked equipment—hooked and pronged teeth in the upper jaw, long sharp teeth that project forward in the lower jaw and glands that shoot poison through these teeth like a cobra. Although not on the list of animals dangerous to man, thanks to its small size, the shrew is a fiend with an insatiable appetite. Not a tunneling animal, it follows the tunnels made by others, using its ferocious tools unceasingly. It will attack and butcher a wood mouse twice its size. The shrew under the forest carpet devours its own weight in food every three hours. All this food energy is spent in furious activity. It even quarrels with its fellow shrews.

Thus, the littlest, meanest wild animal of the forest is an analogue for a scolding woman. On the other hand, the unhesitant ways of this animal with its sharp nose have elicited admiration, as expressed in our word shrewd, from medieval English. Certainly the shrew is smart in its way. One species swims and dives to catch little fishes and even walks on the bottom of a pond digging out spawn from the gravel. Faced by a large fish or a wading bird, it uses its forefeet like propellors, breaks the surface and runs on the water by grasping little bubbles with its feet.

Woodchucks cause the greatest upheaval in the meiofauna provinces. A full-grown woodchuck is about two feet long, stands seven inches at the shoulder and weighs about 10 pounds—it is a clumsy, overgrown squirrel which can't climb trees. This inability to take refuge in high foliage, plus a fatty body and lumbering gait, would have spelled the extinction of woodchucks had not natural selection and the pressure of environment made this animal a powerful tunneler. The woodchuck's tunneling genius is equal to every contingency. Its tunnel apartment house has a 12-inch door surmounted by a pile of earth that is a conspicuous inviting portal proclaiming, "Lodgings for all ethnic groups: rabbits, skunks, opossums, snakes, weasels." This, the best lodging offered to non-burrowers in the forest, is arranged so that visitors cannot disturb the owner.

A typical woodchuck tunnel is 25 feet long. From the big front door with the pile of dirt it narrows and slants down to a depth of about seven feet, then ascends and branches to side apartments. One chamber, lined with herbs, is a bedroom, another room is a toilet where the wood-chuck covers its feces with soil. These winter sleeping quarters, well above the low point of the tunnel, are safe from flooding by heavy rain and melting snow. In addition to the front door, there are two other openings, carefully planned. A back door, convenient in case undesirable visitors are lurking at the main entrance, is fifteen or twenty feet away. There is a pile of dirt here too, but it is well hidden among bushes (nearby bushes are a requisite for a woodchuck tunnel). The third hole is out in the open because woodchucks enjoy basking in warm sunlight. Planned with inscrutable animal intelligence, it offers a quick escape route in an emergency. No pile of dirt reveals it, and its shaft *drops straight down* for several feet before slanting off in a corridor to the main tunnel. A fat lazy woodchuck, having foraged and stuffed itself, sits beside this hole to take the sun. If a sly fox approaches, the woodchuck simply drops out of sight. It vanishes in a split second without running a step.

In the lower part of the leaf carpet leaves do not dry out on every fair day. They are flatter, more compressed and the spaces between them are narrower. Faint gleams of daylight filter in. This is the threshold of perpetual darkness.

Leaf outlines are still generally intact here, but the skeletons are soggy, sticky and colored a dark brown. Gone now is the bright metallic gleam which gave the beautiful colors they had when they first drifted down to the forest floor. Their treasure of vital metal elements such as iron, mag-nesium and calcium has been partially dissolved and leached away. Or-ganic debris, mostly cellulose; slag of lignin and gums, and residues of proteins are still locked in the delicate skeletal form. Yet the leaf skel-etons are slowly sinking, breaking. Some regiments of the bacteria of decay have invaded this area, although the masses of bacteria are deeper down. (Bacteria shun acid soils, and it is somewhat more acid among the leaf skeletons than in the underlying humus.) The humus zone, just be-neath the leaf carpet, nurtures lush jungles of fungi. White mushroom threads and white mildews and molds can be seen when you turn up wet dark leaves or look under logs and stones. But most of the tremendous crops of fungi are invisible to the naked eye.

The bodies of fungi are colorless tubes—exceedingly fine threads which grow so fast that their growth can be seen with the aid of a microscope. They snake in all directions through the labyrinths of wet leaf debris, branching and re-branching, forming extensive networks. Although their threads are exceedingly fine, fungi require ample growing space. They form dense tangles in unlimited, connected tunnels and recesses. They also need sporing room where they can fling off their tiny reproducing spores. The fungi cottons find such accommodations in this level of loose wet leaf skeletons. Moreover, fungi thrive in darkness. They have no chlorophyll, need no sunlight and get their food from the cellulose of the leaf skeletons. Heavy humidity with plenty of oxygen is ideal for them. There is plenty of air and water among the sodden leaf skeletons, so fungi communities in the lower part of the leaf carpet of the deciduous forest enjoy a wonderfully stable habitat.

During summer the white threads of fungi reproduce themselves by elongating, breaking apart, and again elongating. A tiny bit of a thread is as good as a seed. But fungi cotton stops growing when it is chilled. So just before leaf-dropping time in the fall, when cool night air creeps into this part of the forest floor, the fungi produce spores that have thick walls and are cold-resistant for survival.

While tremendous sporing in the larger and airier spaces under the leaves is planting next year's fungi crop, many of the cottony threads are so violently stimulated that they develop highly ornate and enormous structures—colorful mushrooms which pop through the forest floor on a cool night, usually in September and October. The roll call of forest mushrooms includes flamboyant aristocrats such as yellow *Boletus,* purple *Cortinarius,* blue *Lactarius,* red *Russula,* edible *Morel,* and the deadly white ghost known as the destroying angel.

During cool nights when these mushrooms are flaring, the only plant that "walks" independently in the forest, creeps out from under the leaf carpet. It bears the odious name slime fungus and is known to botanists as the *Myxomycete* (Greek for slime fungus).

Trailing speedwell and partridge-berry walk on the floor of the forest —in a sense. Their creeping stems take root at intervals and then sever segments and leave them behind. And walking fern is a graceful pedestrian on north-facing slopes. Its slender frond elongates with a long low arch. When its tip touches the ground a few inches away, it roots, the base of the frond breaks off and the fern is on its way.

But the slime fungus moves its whole body like an animal. After oozing up in a sodden spot of the leaf carpet, it forms a viscous colorless cushion several inches across and then proceeds to poke out extensions and to feel its way along like a giant ameba. The black soggy surface of a decaying tree stump is a favorite promenade because slime fungus engulfs decaying plant stuff, digesting the rotten wood and excreting the waste—a fungus on the prowl. When the freak has had its fill it halts, its soft flexible skin becomes tough and crisp, it turns red, yellow or brown, and gushes spores. Some biologists argue that slime fungus is a member of the animal kingdom because it moves and feeds like a big ameba. Unquestionably it is an exciting plant-animal of the deciduous forest.

Certain fungi weave tough thimbles of their cotton around the root tips of trees, a phenomenon called fungus-root—*Mycorrhiza* in Greek. When first discovered in 1885, the club-shaped mycorrhiza was thought to be a disease of the roots caused by mushrooms that had turned parasitic, an opinion more or less held for half a century. Then science discovered that fungus-roots exert remarkable powers for keeping the dynamic forest soil at a peak of efficiency.

In some paradoxical way a lack of nitrogen, phosphorus, potassium and calcium stimulates fungi to weave their thimbles on root tips as a substitute for root hairs. The tangle of threads multiplies the collecting surfaces of root hairs many times. The fungus imbibes more minerals, takes in more carbohydrates, selects and stores more nourishing solutions than the tree could obtain on its own. In addition, this remarkable fungus eats proteins and excretes ammonia, thus providing its tree with precious nitrogen.

This is not big-hearted generosity on the part of the fungus. The trees pay for these supplies by exuding chemical solutions which vitalize the fungus, causing it to reproduce vigorously. Without this compensation from the tree roots, the fungus would "wither on the vine" and die.

And without fungus-roots the deciduous forest would be less luxurious. Its beautiful evergreen needle associates would be lacking. Pine, spruce, fir, larch, hemlock, red cedar—almost all evergreen needle trees —are dependent on fungus-roots for their well-being. Canoe birches, American hornbeam, hazelnut and the bushes of the heath family, all depend on fungus-roots for their vitality. The big deciduous trees which most often form partnerships with fungi are beech, oak, and black walnut.

The mushrooms which render this service to forest trees are some of the best-known and most beautiful—*Amanita, Boletus, Tricholoma, Lactarius, Cortinarius, Russula* and puffballs. The trees have preferences. Birch often uses fly amanita; white pine likes the milky mushroom; scotch pine prefers boletus, and beech and oak are lovers of puffballs.

People walking in thinned, second-growth woodland may see mushrooms growing in circles, as much as 30 feet in diameter, the famous "fairy rings." They surround a place where a large tree, such as an oak or beech, recently stood and traces of the stump can usually be found in the center of the circle. Fungus roots only grow on the young active root tips which are around the rim of the tree-root system. So fungus roots, which require plenty of air, are located under the outer circle of branches and form a circle whose diameter increases as the tree grows. If the tree dies or is cut down, the changed condition stimulates the abandoned fungus-roots to put up their sporing umbrellas and a fairy ring appears.

The frail, exceedingly slender threads of fungi in the upper layer of the leaf carpet on the forest floor make an entirely different sort of merger that results in some curious forest decorations. In this case the mushroom's partner is an alga, a tiny green seaweed that grows in forest soils. The fungus-alga combination becomes a lichen.

Algae are by no means confined to the oceans as conspicuous sea-weeds. They include pond scums and the light green tresses that wave lazily in stagnant fresh water. They are the jellylike slime that appears in goldfish bowls, the splashes of green on the damp north side of tree trunks in a shadowy forest. The algae that merge with mushrooms are very primitive plants of the forest. They are microscopic, spherical and one-celled—only 1/2500 of an inch in diameter. They exude a gelatin by means of which they often cling together end to end in short chains. Most important, all algae, like seaweeds, contain chlorophyll, the green food-making pigment of leaves.

In the vastness of the forest all sorts of predators capture and devour all sorts of prey, but this encounter between a colorless fungus and a green alga has an extraordinary result. The alga is not devoured. It finds itself in a healthy situation surrounded by the water-holding threads of the fungus. (An alga, above all, must have water.) Moreover, the alga, which must have light to make food, is not in the least shaded by a fungus. Fungus threads are translucent and admit all the light the alga needs. So the alga prospers, its cells divide, its chain lengthens. The fungus, on its part, has the good fortune to find itself embracing a food-making organ, because green algae act like green leaves.

Interdependence is an everyday fact in the life of the forest. Vines grow on trees, ferns on mosses, beechdrops on the roots of beech trees. Some seeds need the chemicals of fungi to germinate. Insects infest green leaves and almost everything else. But the fungus-alga combine is unique in the way it joins two different kinds of plants to create a third kind.

The fabric of a lichen is derived from fungus threads so densely knit, so tightly welded, that they become like tough leather. The green cells of the alga occupy a particular spot just beneath the upper surface of the leathery body. Although the fungus and alga have created another kind of being, strangely enough they do not lose their identities. If they are separated—which happens only when a curious botanist teases them apart under a microscope—and properly nourished, they pursue their separate lives.

A lichen is a highly successful combination, with more power for survival than any other many-celled living thing on earth. It is an air plant in the sense that it takes no nourishment from any living or dead material to which it clings. A lichen on a tree trunk clings to the bark with holdfasts that do not penetrate living cells or hurt the tree in any way. This is the only kind of plant that can flourish in an utterly sterile place. For this reason the lichen played a heroic role in the spread of the forest northward across ice-scoured rocks in the wake of the ice-age glaciers.

A lichen attaches itself to the bare face of a rock by brewing a powerful acid which dissolves rock crystals, and then pokes a tough thread, or holdfast, into the tiny cavity between grains of lime in limestone and crystals of mica and garnet in granite. Even silicate, granite's hardest crystal, is dissolved in time by lichen acid. In this way, the crystals of granite are eventually loosened. A speck of sand results. A bit of organic duff is made. The weathering of rock is promoted and with passing centuries a place is prepared for trees and flowers.

Chemists recognize more than 140 lichen acids to which rock crystals surrender. Such powerful acids would be fatal in the protoplasm of living cells, so the fungus partner generates the acids *outside* of its cells and the alga partner generates alcohol that converts the acids to salt crystals. In this form, reserve supplies of acids are stored *between* the threads of the fungus and their living cells are not harmed.

The salt crystals of lichens reflect the spectrum of sunlight like minute diamonds. This gives lichens their play of color. In silvery lichens the acid-salt crystals are clear. In others they are yellow, orange and bright red in the sunlight, or lichen acid-salts may change from yellow to scarlet as the intensity of light changes.

The indifference of a lichen to heat and cold, wetness and dryness, lies in the utter simplicity of its body and its closeness to the elements. What a vast and complicated apparatus most plants use in contrast to the simple arrangements of the lichen, where two elemental plants work together. The threads of the mushroom absorb and hold water like cotton, and they embrace the algal chains which make food for both by means of the chlorophyll they contain. In terms of survival a lichen is close to perfection. It is more ancient than the forest itself.

Yet lichens are a downright paradox because they ignore important rules which are observed by other kinds of plants in the forest around them. For example, the keystone of inheritance is that generations breed through chromosomes. Chromosomes are visible ribbons of genes in the nuclei of living cells which insure that descendants are true to the species of their parents. Alone among plants, lichens have no genes and no descendants. A lichen does not perpetuate its kind through spore or a seed.

However, lichens do have conspicuous sporing organs, seen as bright red tips or warts, and the surfaces of some are pockmarked with little depressions that are spore cups. Such organs gush spores but they are the spores of the fungus partner only. When one of these germinates, it produces a fungus thread, not a lichen. Lichens solve the problem of propagation in other marvelously simple ways. One is a sort of parcel post device. You often see lichens covered with a sparkling silvery dust. Each grain of dust is a parcel where one green alga cell (often more than one) is tightly wrapped in mushroom threads. This parcel is left on the outside of the lichen, so loosely attached that a breath of wind will carry it off. When it lands, it may sprout. Since the package contains both partners, it sprouts a lichen!

A more conspicuous way of reproducing its kind is for a lichen to break into pieces. Lichens are often brittle when dry, and their loose edges tear apart easily in the wind. Instead of a lichen destroyed, a large number of lichens will be born, for each fragment—provided it contains the magic ingredient of a green alga (and a single cell will do)—will grow a new lichen. By the same token, the tips of the lobes of a large lichen—spread out flat upon a rock or tree trunk—may break off and go right on living independently. Instead of old age withering the body until it dies, the thing shatters itself into many fresh, young lichens.

Moreover, those spores ejected by the fungal partner can put lichens in every nook and cranny of the forest. It might seem mathematically impossible for spores released into the ocean of air to collide with a microscopic speck which happens to be precisely the right partner, but nature loves to take long chances. The spores are produced in astronomical numbers and so are the green algal cells. They float everywhere in the air of the forest and settle invisibly far and wide, filtering down among the leaves on the floor in vast numbers and catching everywhere in the cracks of bark. Thus, by the law of averages, the chances are that the right kind of fungus spore and the right kind of alga will meet.

Nobody ever knows how old a lichen is. One researcher, determined to get data on this subject, staked out a project to measure through the years the minutest changes in size of a conspicuous crust lichen. After 16 years the report concluded, "Not perceptively enlarged." Another patient lichenologist concentrated on the geographic lichen, so named because it looks like a map glued to the face of rock. The report in this case was, "It remained in the same condition for 25 years."

Perhaps the longest period of research on record is the case of a lungwort lichen, a lusty 10-inch species resembling a tawny chamois skin, which likes old oaks. It was observed "to occupy the same area of the tree after half a century." Initials carved in lichens on boulders in north Greenland, where explorers were frozen in for the winter in 1925, were next seen in 1950, and no growth or change in the clean-cut carving could be detected.

Obviously, many lichens do grow bigger when people are not looking. The increase in diameter of a flat rosette lichen is said to average less than 1/10 of an inch a year. Actually lichen size has nothing to do with the passage of years; growth is in direct relation to dampness.

The lichen plant is a beautiful example of surrealist art. It is flat like a leaf, but it has no veins, no bilateral symmetry. Although some stand erect, they are desultory, weak and flabby, with no stem, and lack completely any principle of growth such as the dynamic spiral by which pine cones grow, ferns uncoil and leaves unfurl from buds. Moreover, they have no order of magnitude. A lichen is always mature, ever full-grown. It has no life cycle between birth and death. Born in the forest leaf carpet, a lichen is the healthiest, most unfailing, most fantastic decoration in the forest.

chapter eleven

Humus

JUST below the last faint glimmer of daylight in the layer of the loose leaf carpet begins the most exciting zone of the forest floor. This is the leaf mold zone, the mother of humus.

Leaf skeletons which have descended to this layer have been teased, chewed and gnawed by voracious hosts of millipedes, springtails, mites, beetles and caterpillars and other life forms which attack the debris. Spaces between the broken leaves are much smaller than between whole leaf skeletons, and the fragments are compressed by more weight of water and debris above them. The tight, dark labyrinths of this zone— glittering with moisture and filled with an atmosphere that contains more carbon dioxide than the open air—are filled with luxurious plant life. Fungal threads run everywhere, and algae achieve their greatest populations in this layer.

Unlike the green algae up in the light, which are partners in lichens, these algae do not cling together in chains. They are spherical, colorless, without chlorophyll and they get their energy from the organic juices which bathe them. This wealth of microscopic plant life supports vast populations of fantastic animals which most people never see. Many of them were discovered only in recent years. Their incessant assaults on the organic trash and on each other generates the highest rate of life power output in the forest.

149

Food energy to sustain these underground pastures and their teeming populations of minute animals pours into the leaf-mold zone from many sources. Rain water trickling through the leaf carpet brings solutions of vital minerals. The root tips of trees which stab through this layer secrete amino acids (the ingredients of protein) and vitamins, which attract soil creatures to such extent that they cluster around root tips like iron filings around a magnet.

The most dynamic supply of food for the leaf-mold zone comes from the welling up of bacteria from the black humus just below. Bacteria are nuggets of live food, containing minerals, proteins, enzymes and vitamins. They are relished by fungi which devour them. It is hard to imagine a more lush hunting ground or richer pasture.

The constant influx of elemental food—particularly the refined bacterial nourishment—has made the leaf-mold zone a sanctuary for myriads of bizarre creatures, among which the most ancient forms of life on earth have been discovered.

For example, springtails lived in the Devonian Period, 350 million years ago. Their generations have survived to live in enormous numbers in the leaf-mold zone of the deciduous forest. Springtails are a famous landmark of ancient life, representing insects before their wings evolved. A flip of the abdomen sends them into the air. Some springtails in the forest soil are even more primitive than that. They are blind, white, and less than one millimeter (1/25 of an inch) long. They do not even flip their abdomens.

Springtails hatch in such astronomical numbers that their microscopic babies are the chief food of another very ancient primitive cult, the *Japygidae.* (The name was inspired by a Greek myth. Japyx was the son of Daedalus who lost his wings when the wax which secured them melted in the sunlight.) The blood-thirsty Japygidae in the leaf mold do not seize springtail babies in rudimentary jaws; they use the ancient method of backing up to their prey and seizing it with forceps located at the rear end of the abdomen.

Another large family among these immortals is *Campodea,* a Greek word meaning "resembling a bending caterpillar." This wingless insect never evolved the standard metamorphosis of insects, and when it was first discovered in the soil it became famous as the most primitive insect form on earth. But this title has recently passed to *Protura,* which means "First insects."

Protura are generally invisible when full grown although some giants reach 1/17 of an inch, and are barely discernible to the naked eye. They have stirred excitement out of proportion to their size because *Protura* have the first six-legged insect body in an original state—even before antennae evolved. Antennae are the most important and characteristic of insect organs, and *Protura,* alone of all insects, lack these celebrated sense organs. Yet somehow this physical handicap has been overcome by a creature which has survived for half a billion years to live among the modern luxuries of our deciduous forest.

The discovery of original mock-ups of the insect body flourishing in the forest floor raises tantalizing questions. Why did their evolution cease at this point? How can it be that our microscopes can focus on *Japygidae, Campodea,* and *Protura*—all of which lived on a different kind of planet hundreds of millions of years before there were forest leaves to stock their world with food?

These crude creatures, infinitesimal in size, are the toughest, most successful race on earth in terms of multiplying and surviving. Big-sized animals are far more vulnerable. Multitudes of tremendous and more complicated animals and plants are extinct. The dinosaurs, bulkiest of land animals, exploited the raw wilderness for a hundred million years while the weather was mild. They ate cycad and ginkgo forest trees like hay, tearing them up by the roots and then they devoured each other.

The tongue-fern forest covered all the lands of the southern hemisphere in a former age, and perished utterly when their spores and seeds could not find protection from the cold. We see the sequoia trees, which once grew around the world, flickering out in our time. The eagles that poured off the Palisades of the Hudson River and floated above Henry Hudson's ships are reduced to a few pitiful pairs desperately looking for places to breed.

The two critical points of a life form are the volume of food needed for each member and the availability of nooks for hiding and breeding. In both respects tiny organisms enjoy infinite resources. The fungi, algae and primitive insects which teem today in the floor of our deciduous forests also lived in the worlds of the dinosaurs, tongue-ferns, sequoias and eagles. The *Japygidae, Campodea* and *Protura* could travel an uninterrupted path across the "interstellar spaces" of time, because living space for creatures their sizes was always available. It was probably similar to the area where they are found today—wet, dark, and reeking with vital minerals and organic nourishment.

A teaspoonful of leaf-mold soil contains myriads of hide-aways independent of the shapes of the continents, the temperature of the outer air, gales and glaciers. What has counted most in the survival of these soil creatures since the evolution of many-celled land life began, is that a bit of wet sand, ooze or mud always existed at tide-water in a swamp or bog and from these a chain of similar living places extended unbroken to the warm, humid labyrinths of the forest soil.

Of course something more is needed than a permanent habitat. That something is the innate vitality of the organization of elements we call a living cell. When that marvel was wrought, life began on earth. In the course of ages, cells clung together and became interdependent, creating complicated structures like *Protura,* a sort of stripped-down chassis of an insect. Antennae and wings came with later models. Single-celled beings are more ancient than *Protura.* They move around with long waving hairs, rows of vibrating bristles, or (as in the case of amebas), by flexing their cell and poking out stubby lobes. We call these one-cellers protozoa. They teem in the leaf-mold zone of the forest soil where, like the fungi, they live on influxes of bacteria from the humus.

Myriads of fiendish, exceedingly tiny worms enliven the microscopic corridors of the leaf-mold. Some biologists point to nematodes as the most successful wormlike organisms on earth. The simple transparent body is hardly more than a thread of digestive tract with an oral opening at one end and an anus at the other.

A favorite living place of this fearsome living thread is in the intestines of an animal, where it may be as long as 40 inches. But in the forest soil, their native home, nematodes are only about 1/25 of an inch long, and barely visible. They are free living, eat anything, and are ravenous for root hairs, which cause them to lay eggs. A nematode under observation, fed on a diet of root hairs and soil organisms, laid five times its own weight in eggs in three weeks. Since nematodes must have a film of moisture to slide in, the leaf mold in the forest floor is ideal. If a drought occurs, nematodes are not undone. They simply shrink and form a crisp cyst that encases eggs—eggs that can hatch *after four years* of dryness!

With such extraordinary powers and such ferocious appetites, why don't nematodes dominate the leaf mold zone and destroy the forest? Nature usually checks monopolies by burgeoning populations through

Humus, the cradle of the forest, is quietly made under the leaf carpet in untrod shires of the deciduous forest.

Thousands of tiny traps are suspended from these floating wheel spokes of bladderwort which lives on underwater insects in quiet forest ponds.

Wild geranium flings out its seeds from spiral catapults. The woodland is filled with dynamic spirals of activity and growth.

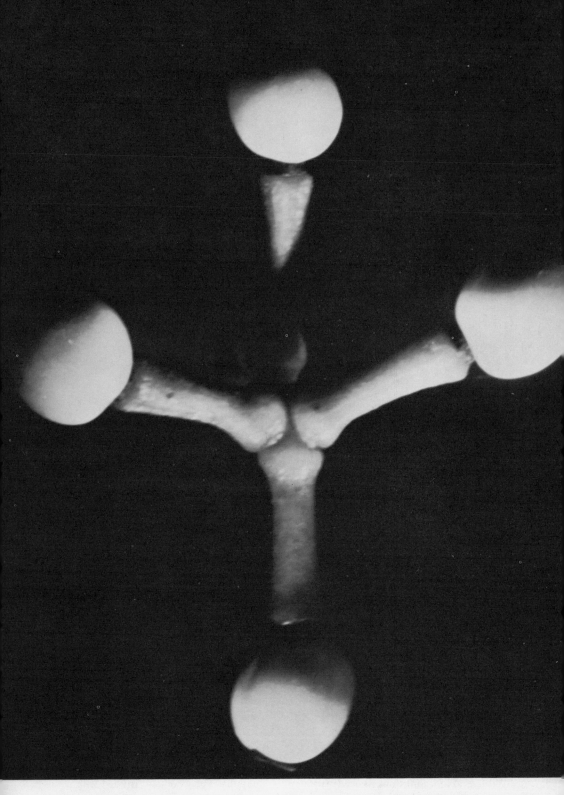

Every item is a separate masterpiece that is precisely fitted into the whole forest operation.

Eccentric water chestnut turns and twists in running water as if probing for a place to plant its seed.

food or water controls and sometimes by a sudden drop in temperature. Freezing clears the forest of armies of insect destroyers overnight. But such conventional checks cannot be used against nematodes in a food-laden saturated leaf-mold zone. Yet they are curbed by an incredible maneuver which scientists could hardly believe when they saw it happen before their eyes.

Picture the tiny worms on the rampage among the cottony threads of fungi in the leaf mold. Until the nematodes turned up the fungi were living normally on solutions of decaying matter. But, in the presence of nematodes, certain mushroom threads assume the duties of constables. They turn from a normal vegetarian diet to become carnivorous with an appetite for nematodes. It would seem to be quite a stunt for a flaccid brainless fungus thread to catch, hold, and devour a strong wiggly nematode. But that is what happens.

Nematodes perspire a chemical called "nemin" that has an astonishing effect on a particular kind of soil fungus. The touch or smell of nemin is like a burglar alarm for the fungus, causing it to put forth short branches with loops at their ends. A nematode's body is formed as a slender spindle, tapering at the ends and thickest in the middle. The inside diameter of the loop of the fungus' thread is slightly less than the diameter of a nematode around the middle. A single fungus may manufacture hundreds of these loops which extend in all directions, presenting an unavoidable array of traps in the path of oncoming nematodes. When a nematode thrusts halfway through one of these loops it becomes stuck; it is deftly lassoed around the middle. The pressure of its body causes the thread of the loop to inflate like a rubber tire. This is fiendishly clever strategy on the part of the fungus thread. By seizing the prey exactly in the middle, the leverage by which a nematode might whip free is cut by half. The nematode cannot break the vegetable thread and is strangled.

The forest soil seethes with insatiable microorganisms that have to be curbed. The balance maintained among their populations is one of the greatest wonders of the soil. It is the incessant carnage, the mass of dead bodies, that makes forest soils nourishing. Fresh waves of microorganisms devour the dead debris and in so doing they tear apart the corpses, then by digesting and excreting they free the vital minerals, the hydrogens, carbons, and nitrogens. Thus, the microorganisms must die and their nuggets of nourishment be dissolved. This is quickly done because they are soft and juicy—much quicker than the lysis of giant tree trunks, leaf skeletons and animal bones.

The soil organisms are the foundations of the chain of life which leads to the forest pageant aboveground. Although microscopic beings may seem to be uniform, their size varies greatly and, as everywhere else, the larger forms find the smaller ones appetizing.

This fact was stated with remarkable insight by Jonathan Swift in 1710, thirty years after bacteria and protozoa were first seen by man. Microorganisms were a social fad of the intelligentsia who gave microscope parties instead of cocktail parties. Swift's was the *bon mot* of the day:

> So, naturalists observe, a flea has smaller fleas that
> on him prey; and these have smaller still to bite
> 'em; and so proceed ad infinitum.

We have been following the leaf skeletons which fell to the floor of the deciduous forest in their slow descent into the ground. In the lower level of the leaf-mold zone, the remains of the leaves and other debris are well pulverized. They have become sticky with water-resisting fats, oils and lignin, which tend to concentrate here where the finer texture of the soil holds them.

Although pulverized and sticky, many materials arriving at this depth of the soil are not yet fully decomposed. What is left is a mash of the most insoluble and unyielding substances such as cutin, the waxy waterproof coating of leaves, and lignin (the tough glue of wood), with an admixture of animal substances such as chitin from the horny skeletons of insects and particles of hairs, hides, hooves, tusks and antlers. These still hold locked-up quantities of carbon and nitrogen, and elements of potassium, sodium, phosphorous, sulfur, magnesium and iron.

Even though there are enough of these elements elsewhere to meet the needs of the trees, the unconverted substances would create a critical shortage of some minerals which are not abundant in the soil yet needed vitally in minute quantities by trees and other plants. Such minerals would be manganese, copper, zinc, boron, nickel and iodine, in the decay-resisting teeth and hooves, hides and hairs.

A small residue of any locked-up elements would be fatal to the forest in the course of time. It would take only a few years of tying up and withholding these minerals to starve all forest plants, and the dead debris on the forest floor would rise up relentlessly and smother the trees. For the perpetuation of life, every last molecule must be loosened from the structures of dead plants and animals. Nature solves this problem easily by creating a microorganism in the forest soil which can break down *every kind* of organic molecule.

The leading demolition crews, of course, are the bacteria of decay. Their most important co-workers when it comes to decomposing cellulose in wood are the mushroom threads (fungi), which are also the enemies of bacteria. In a general way these two big wrecking operators divide up the territory, with the fungi concentrating in their zone in the uppersoil and in more acid ground under evergreen trees. Bacteria do their greatest work deeper in the floor of the deciduous forest, and in nonacid warm damp soil.

What goes up must come down. Sooner or later everything comes down, from the tiniest flower to the most massive tree. All the materials of the forest, including all its wild life, generated above ground by the energy and substance of the plants that rose from the soil, will sooner or later merge in the forest floor. Only a small percentage of elements will escape into the atmosphere in the form of vapors and gases. But their loss is temporary. They will be recaptured by the leaves of future trees.

The standing armies of bacteria and fungi in the soil are the professionals which keep the tearing down in pace with the building up. But the job is tremendous in the face of the annual downfall of leaves, the casting off of bark, buds and twigs, the rain of seeds, pollens and petals, and deposits of flesh, bones and excrement. The job of dissolution, which has to be done to the last molecule, calls for auxiliaries such as the insects that attack the softer materials in the sun-warmed leaf carpet and the olla podrida of protozoa, algae and nematodes.

So what about those horns and hooves, hides and hair that have accumulated in the top soil layers, and could destroy the forest if they accumulated too long? An organism with weird powers is on hand to deal with this problem.

Where the hordes of other soil organisms are frustrated by the all but insoluble and decay-resisting materials, the terrific actinomycetes tackle the job, and the problem melts away. The clumsy name, *actino mycetes* is Greek for ray fungus. Biologists who first caught the glint of these mysterious live things labeled them fungi because of their threadlike bodies that suggest fragments of sun rays reflecting the red, yellow, blue and green bands of the spectrum. But unlike the cotton threads of fungi, these suddenly change their form; the threads break up and act like bacteria. This is one of the most thrilling revelations of the powerful electron microscope. Actinomycetes are so slender that two thousand of them, laid side by side, would be barely visible. They defy classifying, but their place in the system of life is unimportant. It is the chemical powers of these off-beat trouble shooters that counts.

The actinomycetes appear only under certain conditions at certain places. There they boil over chemically, liberating a continuous stream of carbon, nitrogen and other vital elements which pervade their environment. They multiply so rapidly on occasion that their numbers are astronomical, surging to half a billion in a teaspoonful of soil. Their activities can be detected by the haunting fragrance of grass and herbs after a spring shower, of freshly turned earth, and the sweet smell of fresh manure.

But the native home of the actinomycetes is under the leaf carpet of the deciduous forest, and our interest here is in their flashing chemical powers by means of which they attack materials beyond the powers of bacteria, such as the refractory ivory of horns and hoofs and coarse bristles. Moreover, they perform a towering service in controlling the living balance of the forest by a massive devouring of bacteria and viruses.

Because of this chemical prowess the ray fungi have been extracted from their places in the forest soil and given a place in the hall of fame of modern science. Medical research has discovered that this weird soil organism, which makes the forest flourish, is also a boon to mankind—more than two thirds of the antibiotics produced in the United States are derived from these ineluctable trouble shooters.

So, in the course of time, everything that lives in the forest dies, falls to the ground and sinks slowly through the upper zones of the soil, while various races of invisible multitudes feast upon the debris. They tear apart the structures, release locked up elements which then merge to form a fertile jelly that continues the descent into the dark underlying humus.

The depth in inches of each layer of the forest soil, and the length of time it takes to convert debris to humus varies at every locality, according to the kind of trees, slope of the ground, temperature and rainfall, and the type of underlying rock—whether granite, sandstone, limestone, sand or clay. The typical, layered forest soil we have been considering is in fairly level areas. On steep slopes the zones are disordered by erosion. Often there is no soil and tree roots scramble over the surface of bare rocks to squeeze into crevices where the unceasing process of humus making continues on the basis of a few leaves, a little water and a few billion microorganisms.

Regardless of various depths of soil in each location, and whatever upper layers may be missing, the ground under all deciduous forest trees is the scene of invisible multitudes at work, preventing the starvation and smothering of the forest. The processing of fallen leaves and other debris that leads to humus is always being initiated at every spot on the forest floor.

True humus, the lower soil layer (which may be any depth), is a unique stockpile of materials instilled with great power. It contains little or no residue of cellulose or other matter with carbon, nitrogen, sulfur, and other elements entrapped. The operation of freeing them has been completed. Compared to the upper soil layers, humus is dark, quiet and deep, but this does not mean that is good only for tree root anchorage. In a sense, it is the *protoplasm of the forest,* where life energies are mixed and sorted.

Humus, located between the animated zones of the forest floor and the pure minerals in the foundation rock, sand, or clay, receives the materials for its qualities both from above and below. The gels of carbohydrates, enzymes, proteins extracted from the floor debris and the bodies of soil organisms filter down by gravity. Iron, magnesium, calcium and all the vital minerals dissolved in the underground water table are lifted into the humus by capillary attraction, as sap rises in tree trunks. The mixture of carbohydrate gels and mineral elements from rock in humus is the fundamental source of all land life.

But the most dramatic feature of humus remains to be told. If that pregnant mixture were the total of humus, it would be little more than dynamic goo, but a surprise maneuver transforms it into a forest builder. Over and above the rise of mineral solutions from the water table, the humus is pervaded by undissolved *crystals* from the basement rock pushed up from below by water pressure under the weight of soil and the forest itself.

The rocks of the earth's crust are constantly eroding, those deep beneath sediments and soil as well as those exposed on the surface of the ground. In so doing, rock under the soil is pulverized to invisibly small crystals of all shapes and sizes, and jagged with eccentric points and angles. That they do not fit tightly together is the great secret of humus.

Two kinds of crystals, serving two different functions, are classified by size. Those larger than 1/500 of an inch, ranging up to visible grains of sand, are termed coarse. These make a supporting skeleton for humus, give anchorage for trees and stiffen resistance to the tremendous pressures transmitted through the roots when tall trees sway in gales. Without such a skeleton, the humus would collapse as sticky mud, with catastrophic results for the forest. One result would be to block the circulation of water and oxygen which root hairs must have.

Crystals smaller than 1/500 of an inch are called fine—in every sense of the word. They make humus a unique stuff on the face of the earth. The spaces between the fine crystals are too minute for microscopic protozoa and other soil organisms. Fungal threads cannot grow here where there is no room to scatter spores, and not even actinomycetes penetrate for the same reason. This leaves the domain of humus to unrestricted myriads of bacteria. They are the most minute bacteria, ranging from 1 micron down to 1/5 of a micron,* and these incredible bacteria are all dedicated forest promoters. They tend to congregate among root hairs where they die and increase supplies of elements such as nitrogen, sulfur and protein with their corpses. The air in labyrinths of humus is nearly 100 percent humid, and the moisture reeks with carbon dioxide exhaled by those minute bacteria. This gives tree roots a richer supply of carbon than their leaves in the outside air. Carbon gas seems weightless, but somebody with a passion for statistics has calculated that the bacteria in a single acre of humus exhale seven tons of carbon dioxide a year.

The extreme smallness of the crystals increases the air-filled space. The carbon-laden atmosphere is 30 to 65 percent of the volume of humus. With such an open texture, undisturbed humus is never waterlogged. Moreover, the crystals are so extremely minute that they are nearly all surface—and it is in the film of water on their surfaces that the chemical action of humus takes place. This is a recent discovery of electronic science. If water-coated crystals in *one pound* of good humus

---

* A micron is 1/25,000 of an inch.

under the floor of a deciduous forest were flattened out, their surfaces would cover *five acres*—a spread for electronic forces.

Earthworms are the only creatures, other than the deep diggers who bring the outside world with them, that sometimes inhabit the humus homeland of the bacteria. Twice a year, in late spring and late fall, earthworms knock off their work in the upper zones and eat their way as much as four feet downward into the humus. There they sit out the hot dry summer and the cold dry winter. However, it would be hard to disturb anything as small as the humus bacteria. A million in a wormful of soil could ride through an earthworm gut and exit at the rear end without being disturbed in the least. Besides the earthworm, the only other animal reported to enjoy eating forest humus is the gorilla.

The perimeter of the forest soil embraces the whole course of the evolution of land life. In the profound labyrinths of the soil, primordial forms of plants and animals have interlocked their lives with the latest masterpieces of evolution. Vast populations of bacteria, fungi, protozoa and primitive insects which lack wings and even antennae, are living lustily among mammal diggers, spiders, beetles, and the larvae of flies. And somehow the elemental forces which the soil multitudes mobilize mount from the soil in the form of the deciduous forest with all its pageantry.

The emanation of the forest soil is our world. We see its spectacular beauty, the play of light in the foliage, its colorful flowers and birds and sensitive versatile animals. But in our eternal search for an understanding of life, we discover a new dimension in the mysteries of the soil. The living soil is so logically organized—with every essential detail of structure and an interplay of microorganisms, electricity and chemicals. A deficiency (or excess) of any of the microscopic beings is promptly corrected before the imbalance alters or destroys the forest.

The forest and its wild life is vulnerable and can vanish from the land as a result of human folly. On the other hand, since it has survived a half million years, bacteria and other primitive soil organisms appear to be timeless and indestructible. As long as a microscopic speck of vegetable matter is left on earth to nourish bacteria, the evolution of life can start all over again.

It might take a hundred million years to get forests going again, probably countless millions more to install in them creatures resembling animals and birds. But the microorganisms which fill the niches of the biosphere are on the whole unaffected by man. They are ever ready to start life spiraling upward again. Every skyscraper, factory, shopping center and concrete turnpike is the site of a potential forest.

chapter twelve

Conifer Forest

NORTH America has only one consummate deciduous forest. On the other hand, four massive cone-bearing forests occupy by far the greater area of the forest regions of our continent. Consider the sweep and distinction of the four.

The *North Woods* is composed chiefly of red, white and black spruce —but with much balsam fir, larch and arborvitae. This forest rolls from the Maine coast, across the snow belt north of the Great Lakes, then northwest to the Yukon River.

The *Southern Forest* is chiefly loblolly, longleaf, and shortleaf pine (called southern yellow pine), with slash pine that crossed the Caribbean from Central America salting the sandy plains of Florida. This forest occupies the great inland warm sandy belt from Virginia to Texas. Swampy estuaries and bayous on the southern borders are the unique province of bald cypress.

The *Mountain Forest* is dominated by Douglas fir, with enclaves of the world's most majestic conifers—big-tree sequoia, sugar pine, ponderosa pine, western larch, white fir and lodgepole pine. This forest blankets the slopes of inland mountain ranges from northern British Columbia to Mexico.

The *West Coast Forest* is a congeries of conifers that are unique in all the world. The coast redwoods (sequoia), Sitka spruce, Alaska cedar,

Pacific yew, western hemlock, western red cedar (a giant arborvitate) and local colonies of the tallest and most beautiful firs—noble fir on Mt. Ranier, Alpine fir on Mt. Hood, red fir on Mt. Shasta, white fir on the California Sierras. These majestic congregations make a chain along the Pacific coast from Alaska to southern California.

Until 1900, three of the continental conifer forests—the North Woods, the Mountain Forest and the northern half of the West Coast Forest— had not been greatly despoiled, were not well known to the general public and included extensive unexplored areas. At the beginning of the twentieth century, the occupation of the continent and its forest, which had begun 300 years before, was not quite completed. Indeed, so vast and remote were these conifer forests that their total preemption was not completed until the 1950's.

In the main, deciduous and conifer forests are conspicuously segregated. The two types of trees—one with its seeds enclosed in ovaries that become fruits, nuts and berries; the other with its seeds naked on cone scales—cannot interbreed. Nature never bred an oak-pine, or a maple-spruce, and no horticulturist ever will. However, the two types intermingle in transition areas, where we find trickles and tracts of conifers in deciduous forest and deciduous trees among conifers.

The lake region in northern Minnesota has the most dramatic transition forest of the continent. You can almost see the conifers traveling northward, with the deciduous forest on their heels.

A slender, far-reaching extension of North Woods conifers dips into the deciduous forest on the Appalachian range, where red spruce and balsam fir march thirteen hundred miles from New Brunswick all the way to Georgia. Black spruce of bitter northern bogs goes south to West Virginia. A solid stand of red spruce out of the North Woods 800 miles away grows at 4,700 feet on Spruce Mountain in West Virginia. At 4,500 feet on Mt. Marcy in the Adirondacks the forest is 85 percent balsam fir. In the Great Smoky Mountains of North Carolina and Tennessee, the forest above 4,500 feet is red spruce and fir. These peninsulas and islands of conifers are surrounded by an ocean of deciduous forest.

However, this is not intermingling. The conifers are holding the citadels they occupied when the icy white wall stood at New York City and Cincinnati. The deciduous forest marching northward in the valleys and along the lower slopes simply bypassed the high stands of conifers. The motivating principle is the same as for snow-capped mountains in warm areas: 100 feet of altitude amounts to 60 miles north. According to climate, the spruces and firs are still up in Canada.

Somewhat parallel is the situation of large detachments from the deciduous forest—trembling aspen (poplar), birch, willow and alder—in the North Woods and the Mountain Forest. They are so widespread that without them those dark conifer forests would be bereft of their wealth of bird and animal life. These deciduous trees supply the timber for beaver dams, the browse for moose and the foliage and feed for birds—not to mention the birch bark canoes of North Woods Indians. But the two kinds of forest are still segregated. The deciduous trees gather along streams and around ponds in the more sheltered localities, which are warmer and wetter—conditions resembling those in latitudes farther south.

True intermingling does occur occasionally. Aberrant species of deciduous trees, such as bigleaf maple, tanbark oak and golden chinquapin (part oak, part chestnut), live under the redwoods and the other giant conifers of the West Coast Forest. White pine and hemlock are congenial to the deciduous forest. Red cedar (a juniper) is the state tree of Tennessee. It is found from New England to the Gulf of Mexico. These conifers are naturalized citizens, but with an alien preference for hilly, rocky ground, shallow soil on hillsides and sandy patches.

I see in this trend an evolutionary phase. The disparate trees are in the process of changing their natures, each kind adapting by natural selection to conditions normal for the other. The most important change is chemical: they are modifying the acid-alkaline requirements of their roots. White pine, hemlock, and red cedar roots, unlike those of typical conifers, are gradually becoming tolerant of the deep, nonacid humus which nourishes white oak, hickory, and ash. Other evidence of evolution can be seen in the soft, fluttery needle foliage of white pine and hemlock. Many hemlock needles are flat ovals which lie on the youngest twigs, not long, sharp, out-thrusting needles. Hemlock cones are also comparatively plump, with thin, pliant scales. Red cedar's cones are facsimiles of pulpy, light blue berries. Technically they are cones, and their seeds are not in ovaries. "Juniper berries" are well known as a flavoring for gin.

So the few intermingled conifers and deciduous trees seem to be showing us a superb time-lapse movie about the evolution of trees. But in our split second of time (compared to the forest) we can see only a single frame. Perhaps in a million years there will be a forest more stalwart than the coniferous, more lovely than the deciduous.* Meanwhile conifer and deciduous forests remain two distinct expressions of tree life on earth.

Consider their contrasting effects on people. The deciduous forest, burgeoning with luxurious wild life, attracted animals and men like a magnet. When the Indians, whose ancestors entered the continent via the Bering land bridge, arrived in the broadleaf woodlands they quickly spread all through it, following waterways and animal trails. When white men arrived, according to John Collier, former U.S. commissioner of Indian affairs, there was not a square mile of the forest between the Atlantic and the Mississippi that was uncrossed by Indian trails. This forest was so vast, so baffling and different from any forest they had ever seen in the Old World that settlers did not move into the depths of the Appalachian forest until the last half of the eighteenth century.

Then the deciduous forest became the home of the pioneer backwoods-man. It was under, above and all around him. Wherever he settled, his two-acre clearing had deep rich humus that took care of his family. Making the clearing provided him with timber for his cabin, his furniture, and his tools. A spring of the purest water bubbled unfailingly beside his door. Fish splashed in the nearby pond and wild turkeys, that like a clearing, arrived to gobble and strut about his property. His son at the age of twelve was as good a shot as dad—and deer, bobcat, possum, rabbit and quail were only a few steps away.

The man with his axe took trees of a forest with myriads of trees, like stars in the sky, and, as he did, the forest was raising a dozen more trees just across his dirt road. The dirt road disappeared in a thicket, circled a boulder, detoured around a tree too big for an axe to bother, descended to run beside a brook and pass under an overhanging cliff. It had some mudholes for a while after a downpour, and sometimes a heavy tree trunk toppled across it, but there was always a way around and such things are a slight matter to a man on horseback, or even to a horse and cart.

Unlike the conifer forests, the broadleaf forest offered a variety of beautifully grained woods, and the different qualities of tree trunks inspired skills that developed a breed of men and a tradition that was distinctly American. Pioneer settlers quickly recognized the working qualities and strengths of the many kinds of wood at hand. The first

* Not, of course, if the most dangerous animal that ever appeared in the forests succeeds in his "conquest of nature."

settlers who followed the stony cuts of fast streams across the Appalachians and fanned out in the Ohio, Kentucky and Tennessee watersheds were men of the trees. They knew that oak, hickory and walnut are hard to split, and thus make the best wagon parts and tool handles. The light-colored wood rays in oak, walnut, and maple, with graceful swirls that darken when exposed to air, make handsome furniture that lasts for generations. The straight-grained logs such as ash, basswood, tulip tree and poplar are easy to work. Ash, tough and elastic, makes the best bows and arrows and good hoe and rake handles; basswood and poplar split easily but are fine for building a shed in a hurry.

Everyone knew the best firewoods. Oak, hickory, and crab apple, dried in the air for a few months, are excellent and do not pop dangerous sparks. Birch, maple, cherry, and crab apple make very hot small-sized fires, that are easily controlled and fine for cooking. Willow and walnut burn very slowly, but willow makes the best charcoal. Freshly cut ash can be heaped on the fire without being seasoned. (The ash log contains an inflammable oil similar to olive oil. Its tree is a member of the olive family.)

American chestnut, an aristocrat of the deciduous forest, virtually swept away in our time by a fungus disease from Asia, played a major part in the lives of the settlers (including Abe Lincoln). The wood fibers of chestnut do not interlock (interlocking grain makes maple, oak and hickory tough and strong, but almost impossible to split), nor is the chestnut grain perfectly straight. Chestnut graining undulates like a shaken rope, with waves that run the length of the log. It is very strong yet it can be split the full trunk's length with a single wedge. One chestnut log gives a dozen pieces twenty feet long that can't be "broke"—for a split rail fence.

The settlers cleared the trees to plant their crops, surrounded their holdings with a split rail fence and had a farm. This was the home place in the deciduous forest for a hundred years while the forest stood intact, unassailable until the wonderfully forested states of Ohio and Indiana were converted into farmland during the last half of the nineteenth century—and the deciduous forest, having taken care of seven generations of Americans, suddenly melted away.

The symbols of men in the deciduous forest are the axe, the corn-patch, the split rail fence, a dog, a cow, a woman in the cabin and children. In the conifer forest the symbols are the canoe, showshoes, fur-bearing animal traps, the spoor of bear and moose, a trading post and a lonely campsite. The trees of the conifer forest offered shelter and fuel, but no special services like those of deciduous forest trees. The conifer forest is a vast setting for fish-laden waterways and hiding places for animals, where all trees look alike.

Instead of being backwoods settlers, the men of the conifer forests were transients. They were *les voyageurs des bois,* the travelers of the woods—hunters, fishermen, trappers, pursuers of wild life, always going somewhere, never settling down except for a season in a trading post where they could contact passers-by who came that way in canoes and on snowshoes.

Considering the origin of the conifers in a bygone era, and their very ancient needle-cone equipment for survival, it would not have been surprising if today conifer forests were outmoded, close to extinction, with only a museum value. To the contrary, we see four rugged conifer forests, practically indestructible,* in possession of most of the forest land of this continent.

Yet the conifer forests have a solemn, old-fashioned aspect in hustling, modern America. They are recognized as magnificent mines for timber and paper pulp. The chief meaning of the conifer forests to urban multitudes is that of temporary adventure in a setting of lakes, streams and spectacular mountains. Genuine forest life is hardly known, little thought of, remote.

True, a few grizzlies of tall tales still lurk among the silent columns of Douglas fir, sugar pine and Sequoia, and in the conifer forests of Alaska. A cougar may occasionally crouch on a limb arching over the trails of a mule deer, ready to hurl itself like a rocket, and somewhere a marten chases a squirrel through the interlocking branches of the spruces; and a fisher, the fastest treetop traveler of all animals, chases the marten. These animals turn to the shadowy conifer forest only for stalking and cover. Their browse is in the sunlit spots and they thrive in the openings. A dense continuous conifer forest is almost a biological desert. As we have seen, the support of both its birds and animals comes from the deciduous colonies which line shores and crowd bogs with birch, aspen, willow, alder, blueberry, crowberry, bearberry, rushes and water-lilies.

In 1933 the tragic Tillamook forest fire wiped out 250 thousand acres

---

* Unfortunately, this is a euphemism, when one considers the number of conifers being transformed into white rivers of paper pulp, up to 22 feet wide, making "rapids" over ten thousand Fourdrinier rollers.

of superb timber in Oregon's largest remaining province of continuous virgin forest. Newspapers all over the country lamented the appalling loss of timber and wild life, but the loss of wild life was not great. A ranger said that before the fire he had walked in the Tillamook forest from daylight to dark seeing no sign of animals or birds except an occasional hermit thrush or wood wren.

The elemental nature of a conifer forest is seen in its lack of deviation. A conifer tree is always made of wood with an ancient, uncomplicated pattern of graining. Even the seedling is woody, in contrast to deciduous trees whose seed sprouts are soft, juicy herbs. Conifers are never climbers or runners, and rarely bushy. They are absolute trees.

The conifer trunk grows straight from ground to tip without forking. Branches thrust out at right angles in regularly spaced whorls, giving a conifer the typical form of a sharp spire. The clean-cut triangle form came down from an age when there was less competition, interference and confusion in the surroundings. The root system is designed with the same regular simplicity as the trunk system, around a central tap root.

All conifers wear a badge which strikingly displays their ancient pedigree—the dynamic spirals of their cones. The diameter of each coil increases at a constant rate with each turn in what mathematicians call a logarithmic spiral as distinguished from the spiral of Archimedes which is that of a coiled rope. The dynamic spiral permits a tree to grow at one end while increasing its all-over size without changing its proportions.

This basic phenomenon of life has been analyzed in one of the most interesting classics of biology of our time, *On Growth and Form* by D'Arcy Wentworth Thompson (Macmillan, 1942), which discovers the play of this spiral everywhere in living things—in seashells, spider webs, the center of a daisy, the curve of a beaver's tooth or an elephant's tusk. It is so elemental that it can be glimpsed in the curve of a sea wave just before it crashes, and in the spiral galaxies of outer space. Whereas the dynamic spiral is often obscured by eccentricities of evolution in elaborate forms of plants and animals, the conifers retain its primitive simplicity in their cones as well as in the outline of the tree, which reflects the structure of the cones.

This transcendent quality of the conifers has been beautifully expressed by a poet in six words: *"Trifles deleted and the strength recorded."* *

* *This Instant Joy,* Mary Ballard Duryee (Pageant Press, 1958).

The cone of a conifer is a remarkably simple reproductive organ. It is tough, durable and works deliberately. It has no soft ephemeral parts like stamens and pistils and no ovary. Two seeds—no more, no less—lie naked at the lower end of each hard woody scale that is curved upward like a scoop so that wind-blown pollen, landing on it, slides down to the seeds.

The scales are arranged around a central axis like the steps of a spiral staircase. Since scales expand steadily as they grow from the bottom of the cone upward, lower ones are the widest and largest, while those at the top are small. This gradation gives the cone its graceful tapering form. While seeds are ripening, their scales are tightly sealed. When they are mature—in one to two years—the resin which glues the scales together melts and they swing down and open wide. Such a fruit can take its time. There is no juicy flesh or green husk that ripens and rots.

Moreover, a tight spiral provides for maximum production in minimum space. The scales are so placed that one is never directly above another in the coil just below. There is no overlapping, no interference. Each seed gets an equal share of air, moisture and light. This advantage of the spiral structure is also enjoyed by the needles which spiral out of the twigs, the twigs which spiral out of the branches and the branches which spiral out of the trunk.

The needle-leaf of a conifer, the food-making organism, is as primeval in its way as the cone. It contains chlorophyll as broadleaves do, but the needle is woody and tough, protected from decay by resin and heavily coated with weatherproof wax. The typical conifer needle is as durable as the cone, yet it is as truly a leaf as are the broad deciduous kinds. It grows by increasing in length without widening. The woody central vein of a broadleaf grows in the same manner; if it were the whole leaf it would resemble a conifer needle. The widening of deciduous leaves is achieved by large soft sap-laden cells that must do their work in a few weeks and die. The long strings of green cells inside a pine needle are so deftly sealed in wood and wax that even expert foresters admit they cannot tell whether a green needle is alive or dead.

Yet a needle leaf cannot be a permanent fixture because it gradually becomes overloaded with resins. Conifers too must shed their leaves—some every year, some every two or three years—and replace them with fresh new ones. Needle leaves fall off the conifers more or less continuously throughout the year but never all at once, so that there are always enough needles to provide a green canopy. Hence they are called evergreens.*

The salient advantage of the needle-type leaf is that extremes of hot and cold weather do not affect it. Moreover it is designed to slow down transpiration, the loss of water from the tree. On a warm sunny day a pine tree exhales one tenth the amount of water transpired by a broad-leaf the same size. By conserving water, and also because its needles are unaffected by freezing, conifers can live through the desert dryness of northern winters when the temperatures are below freezing for months at a time.

This ability to resist dryness and cold makes it possible for conifer forests to grow on the sandy land of the south where summers are dry and hot, and high on mountains where winters are dry and freezing. Needle leaves can build forest wherever there is enough sand to cover a root, regardless of hot or cold air. A forest of Scotch pine grows in a spot in northern Siberia where winter temperatures are 50 or more degrees below zero for weeks on end.

A surprising discovery has recently been made about the way needle-leaf trees survive in arid places. Conifers are drought-resistant not only because their needle leaves reduce the escape of water, but also because they can reverse this process. Careful tests have shown that the needles of ponderosa pine in the mountain forest absorb traces of moisture from the air, and this moisture somehow passes down through the tree *and is expelled through the roots into dry ground*. Ponderosa pines are thus not entirely dependent on rainfall and snow. By reversing the normal process of taking water out of the ground and expelling it into the air through the leaves, they can capture the night dew and the moisture of light clouds and send it to their roots. This gives ponderosa the ability to raise its superb forests with massive boles towering 200 feet, despite exposure to cruel drying winds on cold high mountain sides.

Similar tests were made on Jeffrey pine, an invincible conifer that grows in bare sand on the High Sierras of California. Out of the raw elements in its hostile environment, this marvelous tree produces needles like slender daggers, almost a foot long, and 10-inch cones. Jeffrey pine, like ponderosa, can take moisture from the air, and send it down into

* Two American conifers are not evergreen. Tamarack (larch) of the North Woods, and bald cypress of our southern states drop their leaves in the fall.

the ground. With only a little moisture these massive conifers can live where herbs and broadleafs would shrivel and die.

That little matter of conifer seedlings being made of wood is another important arrangement for their survival during a drought. Because the needles, twigs, and main stem of the seedling are composed of wood they do not wilt and collapse; their system of pipelines remains erect and intact until moisture arrives. The collapse of its succulent stem is fatal to a deciduous tree.

The conifer patents for survival were perfected in remote abysmal epochs between the Age of Reptiles in the Upper Jurassic and the proliferation of the deciduous forest in the Upper Cretaceous, a span of 100 million years—time enough to perfect and field-test such survival mechanisms as cones and needles.

The conditions that evolved this highly successful type of tree were the same as those which caused the downfall of the dinosaurs. The rise of mountain chains interfered with the distribution of rain. Lakes evaporated, leaving vast areas of dry sand and rock, changing the pattern of prevailing winds that brought cold weather to the south. While the reptiles were disappearing, the conifers were being pushed around, pressured, challenged by bitter weather and dry stony land surfaces. Changes in environment always stimulate evolution. The outcome in this case, the durable cone-needle combine, represents a triumph of plant life on earth.

There are four isolated species of pine living in American forests today (and nowhere else on earth) which are dramatic exhibits of survival by the cone-needle trees. A few miles north of San Diego, California, the hills facing the Pacific Ocean have an arid and treeless aspect. For centuries they have been exposed to the full force of Pacific storms which have eroded them in fantastic patterns, the sandstone tinted with pulverized iron ore and volcanic scoria. No less fantastic than the canyons which the waves and wind have sculptured is a little oasis of conifers there, a single and final refuge on earth of the unique Torrey pine. Its gray-green needles are 10 inches long, stiff and twangy, and they vibrate like violin strings when the wind strikes them. The weird needles radiate in clusters at well-spaced angles so that each cluster forms a large ball. When these balls of needles reflect the sunlight, the sprawling, contorted branches appear to be holding out electrified pinwheels.

The branches may form complete loops in the violent winds that attack the Torrey pines from every direction. Some of the trees lean far out from the rim of their canyon, but they do not fall. The writhing branches on the upper side grow in a direction that brings the trees into balance. And still another tactic helps the half-tumbled Torrey pine survive in its precarious position. In some places where undermining by sea waves has toppled the canyon side, a curious apparition is seen where the bulges of great roots are exposed. The trees have sent their root cables 30 or 40 feet down into that hard, nearly sterile, stony ground.

The typical conifer spire is staccato, inflexible, with tiny branches and rigid needles of metallic sharpness. This is the character of the conifers of the big forests which reflect the main stream of the race through the ages. The grove of Torrey pines represents an archaic divergence. They have been separated from the main stream long enough for their wood to lose its straight grain and evolve fantastic loops. This did not change its conifer nature and is a peculiar example of the efficiency of the cone-needle survival mechanism.

Whitebark pine is another fascinating example of a conifer's ability to survive almost any emergency. When a prehistoric forest retreated, the eccentric whitebark pine was left stranded on high mountain slopes touching the glaciers, where violent winds shaped the boulders, and the sterile ground was frozen hard most of the year. Such a desperate situation could have been common before the mountains were lowered by erosion and the weather moderated.

High up on mountains the whitebark pine communes with the purest air, the clearest sunlight, and the crystals in rocks. Its branches and twigs are so flexible that the fiercest wind cannot hurt them. You can tie knots in its twigs, which are segmented like a backbone. Each segment is about a quarter of an inch long, and represents a whole year's growth. Thus whitebark, by dint of its cones and needles, is created with meticulous regularity by the rhythm of the years; you can count 25 annual bumps on two inches of twig. Long needles stream together with a graceful swish. The trunk of the whitebark pine lies horizontal on the ground, sprawling over flat rocks like a serpent, with loops that occasionally slip over the rim of a cliff and swing like festoons in mid-air.

Evolution, eternally pragmatic, taught whitebark pine that the best way to resist the wind pressure was to lie down and scramble among the boulders. So that its wood be supple enough to perform the necessary contortions, resins were left out. Standard pine bark is darkened by such resins, which exude from cells just under the bark. There are hundreds of resin pockets to a square inch in other pine trees, but none in whitebark pine. The result is that the outer cells of the trunk are empty and their myriad of microscopic air spaces reflect light in all directions. This makes the bark white like that of the famous canoe birch. Its inaccessible location high on mountains and its twisted prostrate form which disqualifies it for timber, safeguards whitebark pine against ravishing by man.

In the high valley of the Siskiyou Mountains in southern Oregon a nondescript forest of medium-sized pines attracts the eye because the trees there are all of the same age and height. It looks like the reforestation project of a paper company. It is, indeed, a reforestation project in an opening where fire had cleared the land. But this reforestation is carried out by the conifers themselves. These are knobcone pines which seal their seeds inside an airtight, waterproof cone where their embryos can sleep like living mummies for half a century. The cone is as hard and heavy as rock. If you try to scratch it with a fingernail, it feels like granite. On typical pine trees, cones grow high in the canopy or near the outer ends of branches, thrusting outward at right angles to the branch on which they grow. This arrangement assures the distribution of seeds over a wide circle when the cones open. Not so knobcones. They appear in threes, set at steep, down-turned angles low down on the trunk. A cone first pokes through the bark horizontally, but as it grows it steadily bends down, so that a mature cone with ripe seeds actually hugs the trunk. As a result of this tight bending, the cone makes a beautiful curving spiral pointing down.

Thereafter, nothing happens. The cones remain like iron fixtures tightly fastened to their trunks. Their scales remain closed, the seeds locked up. Eventually, a knobcone pine covers its cones, the expanding trunk growing around them. If the tree dies, its cones remain attached to (or inside) the dead trunk. The seeds inside them remain vital indefinitely.

Sooner or later comes a forest fire. This is what these outlandish cones have been waiting for. They explode like popcorn, and a new forest is planted. Dead trunks in the rubble on the forest floor may participate in the reforestation while the fire is still burning and the embers hot. This is why a knobcone pine forest is composed of trees all the same age and size; they have all been planted at the same time after a burn.

Knobcones are not the only pines with built-in fire insurance. Lodge-pole pines of the Rocky Mountains and the jackpines around the Great Lakes have cones that do not open automatically when the seeds are ripe, but which do pop open when intensely heated. But lodgepole and jackpine do not rely solely on forest fires for planting their seeds. They shed their cones, which are not as hard as granite, and the seeds sprout freely in the course of time after the cones disintegrate.

chapter thirteen

The Tallest, The Oldest, The Strangest...

THE life spans of individual trees are not important in the economy of the forest. Trees are cone and fruit bearers, propagators of forests, and a forest is well served when a mature tree, having dispersed its seeds, disappears and leaves a dozen seedlings in its place. This is the normal procedure in every healthy forest. However, certain impressive and dramatic conifers disdain their seedlings and act as if they have the secret of eternal life.

The dawn of human civilization occurred around 4 thousand years ago when Hammurabi scratched his code of laws on a slab of clay, which was baked and buried under desert sand in Babylonia. At that same time some conifer seeds slid out of the cones of their parents—sequoias and pines—and became buried in the duff on the floor of their forests. The seeds sprouted and the trees grew and grew. After a thousand years, when Babylon fell to the Persians, they could have had trunks several feet in diameter and 150 feet tall. They grew and grew—while the ancient Egyptian civilization faded, while the Greek and Roman empires rose and fell, all through the Dark Ages and while the whole history of Europe was being written.

Some of those same trees are still growing today, where they have dwelt in easy balance with their surroundings through all those centuries

181

of human history. They are so isolated on high mountains that there is no record of any man seeing the sequoias until a hunter named Dowd chased a grizzly bear up a mountain in the High Sierras of California in 1852.*

Until recently the General Sherman big-tree sequoia was believed to be the oldest living thing on earth. To all appearances it *should* be the title-holder, with a trunk as massive as a fort, and with the base of that trunk occupying 3,319 square feet of California real estate. Hoary furrows in its bark are two feet deep. It is now known that General Sherman had reached its 3,327th birthday when Columbus reached the new world.

How can this be calculated?

Previously the ages of ancient sequoias had been estimated in very round figures as over 4 thousand years. Then recently scientists invented a way to find the ages of trees almost to the year, by extracting a slender ring core running from bark to center without hurting the tree. This extracts a pencil (18 feet long in the case of General Sherman) with the annual rings of the trunk all lined up to be studied and counted through a microscope to the pinpoint center that denotes the first-year seedling. The widths of the rings along the pencil show the succession of wet and dry years which can be correlated with the centuries of history through which the tree has lived.

General Sherman's corrected birth certificate now reads 3,800 years— a few centuries less than had been estimated. But what do a couple of centuries matter? The lives of these old monarchs are outside the order of human life span. However, they now have a competitor for the title of oldest living thing on earth.

* When the rumour of Dowd's discovery reached the saloons in Sacramento, a man with a sense of showmanship organized a party to investigate. The spectacle was so unbelievable that they formed a syndicate to ship a big-tree log east so that the rest of the world would pay to see it. But men who could swing a good axe made little impression on a trunk 100 feet in circumference, covered by bark 2 feet thick. They laid aside their axes and four men worked for 22 days boring holes to upset the monster by driving wedges—and the first big-tree sequoia came crashing down. A section finally reached New York where it created a sensation. After that the smart promoters found it more profitable to transport bark in the round than a section of trunk. So another big tree was wedged over after a month of labor and painstakingly stripped of its vast curve of bark, which was sold for a thousand dollars to exhibitors in Europe. Then a double bowling alley was built on the prostrate barkless log.

In 1956 Dr. Edmund Schulman of the University of Arizona, brought back from a field trip in the White Mountains (on the California-Nevada border) ring cores from bristlecone pines. After careful laboratory study, he announced that some bristlecones, living in that bitter, isolated location were 4,500 years old. This was no mere estimate. It was based on counting rings with precision instruments, one year at a time. The round figure was used because of confusion in the center of the trunk, where wood rings of sapling years are compressed by pressures of wood sheaths added through millennia. So the sequoias were unexpectedly nosed out as front runners in the Methuselah competition.

When the tiny seed * which contained the embryo of General Sherman split open and sprouted in the High Sierras, certain bristlecone pine trees, 80 miles away, 10 thousand feet up—almost two miles above sea level—were in the full vigor of youth, aged 500 years.

Delving into the long history of the sequoias and bristlecones by means of the weather calendars in their tree rings and the geologic records in the rocks of their mountains, a fabulous tale unfolds. Although the two mountain ranges are less than a hundred miles apart, they were uplifted at different geologic times. The White Mountains were in existence long before the Sierras, and they supported a great conifer forest that included tough bristlecone pines. When, in a later epoch, orogeny (geologic mountain lifting) raised the peaks of the High Sierras between the White Mountains and the Pacific Ocean, this intruding range intercepted rain-laden clouds from the Pacific carried inland by prevailing westerly winds. Thereupon, with imperceptible slowness, paced by the uplifting High Sierras, the eastern sector of the forest on the White Mountains lost its water supply; it was disrupted by thirst.

Today people who climb to the snowfields of Mt. Whitney and face the east see a shimmering desert of yellow sand stretching to Death Valley. Northeast, the White Mountains eighty miles away look as bare of vegetation and as arid as the rest of the landscape. The distant ranges are a misty blend of blue sky and yellow sand, except where a summit, almost as high as Mt. Whitney, reflects a white snow field.

Just below that solitary white patch, at around 10 thousand feet, is the spot where the time-battered forest of bristlecone pines is sitting out eternity. To be left high and dry in a rocky desert, alternately sunburnt

* A big-tree sequoia seed is less than ¾ inch long, and 3 thousand of them weigh only an ounce.

and frozen through 4 thousand years after all their associates have disappeared, and yet live on, is a miracle of survival.

The bristlecone trees are gaunt runts. Many which died more than a hundred years ago are still standing, their skeletons silver gray, splintered, burnished by blowing sand. They do not rot because even bacteria of decay cannot tolerate such aridity and because oxygen is at a premium at such an altitude. But thanks to the seepage of water from the snow patch and a breath of moist air in the night, this sparse relic of a forest not only lives but produces sturdy embryos, as shown by a number of young trees scattered about.

The Indians knew about these old bristlecones. Many of their artifacts have been found in the area, but the mysterious tribe that found refuge in that lofty hideout has vanished, and the lonely old bristlecone forest was unknown in modern times until about 15 years ago when an intrepid, mountain climbing forest ranger noted in his report that he had measured one with a diameter of 12 feet. In 1950 the U. S. Bureau of Naval Research, in cooperation with the University of California, established a high altitude research station on the 14,242-foot peak of the White Mountains. Their trail, which passes near the bristlecone forest, is said to be the highest vehicle road in the United States. Dr. Edmund Schulman reached the trees in this way when he made his sensational discovery that these vigorous derelicts are considerably older than the magnificent sequoias.

Perhaps we witness here the last flicker of life in the evolutionary extinction of a forest. What irony if the bristlecones survive, while the forests of redwood and Douglas fir, and the North Woods are destroyed by man.

As long as the ancient White Mountains were rain catchers, they supported a fine conifer forest that included sequoia, white fir, ponderosa pine and sugar pine, which spread westward and also covered the low rolling hills that were destined to be uplifted to create the High Sierras. As the new range rose slowly and relentlessly, the original broad forest was severed by a desert valley. Its eastern part on the White Mountains grew sparser and retreated up the slopes, the grim aridity of the valley close behind. Surviving trees reached toward the snowfields seeking moisture, until at long last the eastern marches of the forest were gone— except for the few indomitable, light-loving bristlecone pines.

Meanwhile, the western part of the forest, high on well-watered mountain terrain, flourishes where canyons resound with turgid streams from melting snows. The profound changes that brought an abundance of swirling mineral solutions and a play of sunlight stimulated the living cells to grow colossal conifers. Big-tree sequoia has fit company where white firs tower 200 feet, ponderosa pines 230, and sugar pines reach a height of 85 feet before branching, then soar upward to 245 feet. The biggest pines in the world, sugar pines, often have trunks eighteen feet in diameter and their cones are 20 inches long. The sugar pines look like monarchs defying the rest of the forest, but big-tree—which John Muir called "the very god of the woods"—stands massive, imperturbable.

Big-tree in the Sierra Mountains and redwood on the California coast are both called sequoia,* and both bear the tribal stamp of vast size. However, they should not be confused at all, if only because their forests are a hundred miles apart. They grow in different kinds of ground and breathe different air. Big-tree is a mile to a mile and a half above sea level where there is less oxygen and the air is bitter cold at times. It receives and has more ultraviolet light, and 10 to 15 feet of snow piles up around its base in winter. Redwood is near sea level, in foggy valleys where there is no freezing, no snow.

The two sequoias have different styles of hugeness. Big-tree has a much thicker trunk, up to 35 feet in diameter, and its branches reach far out horizontally, giving it a mammoth spread. Lumbermen see enough board feet in one big tree to build eighty 5-room houses. In contrast, redwood has tall, slender proportions. Its 20-foot trunk diameter is massive enough to hold up a column 300 feet tall—but its wood would make far fewer than eighty 5-room houses. Redwoods are the tallest trees in the world. There was no reliable way to measure a standing redwood's height to the inch until recently. The champion, according to official announcement in 1964, rises 359 feet, 3⅗ inches above the ground.

Down where a man stands, a trunk twenty feet in diameter seems too big, too permanent, too immobile, to be a living thing. When you put your head way back and look up at it, the lines of the trunk converge like a railroad track in the distance. People are awed by the height of the columns of the Parthenon at Athens. It would take ten of those

* Named for a famous Cherokee Indian chief. Needles and cones of the two sequoias are altogether different, and botanists have recently changed their generic names. Big-tree is *Sequoia-dendron giganteum,* redwood is *Sequoia sempervirens.*

columns set end to end to reach as high as a redwood tree. Yet the incredible redwood pillar is lightly poised; it stands firm and unquivering on the floor of a valley where the air among the boles is still and rampaging winds are far away.

This sense of delicate balance is augmented by a bulge at the base of the trunk where it folds under, making a shadow which gives the impression that the redwood is detached from the ground and floating a few inches above, or the bulge may strike you as a cushion holding up the tree. However, it is more truly comparable to a bulging muscle, where the sinews of the wood are strained and taut resisting the appalling pressure at the foot of the tree from the downward thrust of the tonnage above.

The extreme tallness of redwoods is the result of their location in deep valleys between steep mountainsides, where most of the sunlight comes from directly overhead. Everybody with house plants on a window sill has seen how they grow in the direction of maximum light. By the same token, redwood trees reach up and up, literally pulled by the light directly above them. At the same time, the massive roots head downward and, since the sediment at the bottom of redwood valleys is deep, redwood anchors may plunge to at least a hundred feet underground.

A lot of water is needed to provide sap for the huge trunks of the redwoods, but due to the peculiarities of ocean currents the redwood sector of the coast is not usually well watered. An annual rainfall of thirty-five inches is not sufficient for these tremendous trees. But the redwoods have an hydraulic mechanism that is a mechanical wonder for extracting a large volume of water from the fogs that roll in from the sea at night.

At sunset the canopies of the redwoods, which had been warmed by direct sunlight, cool off quickly. Within an hour, the inevitable fog arrives and, coming in contact with the high, chilled twigs, needles, and cones, it condenses and falls like gentle rain. The tallness of the trees greatly increases the efficiency of this water-collecting mechanism. Where condensing surfaces of twigs, needles and cones are one above the other in a tower, loss of water by evaporation is reduced and the "rain" is increased. Moreover, the water dripping all night long from the canopy falls around the base of the trunk in a circle that outlines the circumference of the roots. (The spread of a tree's roots usually corresponds to the spread of the canopy.)

Bald cypress forests fill vast swamps and bayous of our Southwest with fantastic wildlife. This tree grows nowhere else in the world.

Bald cypress knees thrusting through swamp are curiosities which science has been unable to explain.

Biggest living thing on earth. General Sherman sequoia trunk is 36 feet thick at base, 272 feet high, despite top broken off by lightning.

The water from mist is estimated to multiply by two or three the amount of water available to the redwoods from rainfall. The ancient redwoods have survived only on the California coast where the tree canopies, near the ocean, are suddenly chilled and heavy fog rolls over their valleys at night.

The first news of the redwoods came from people who were not looking for a forest and who were greatly upset by the sight of this one. A party of forty-niners who had come up from Sacramento, were cut off from their supply base on the Trinity River by torrential rains and floods. Their only chance to survive was to head westward to the coast—seventy miles distant through unexplored country. Twenty-four men set out, but conditions were so overwhelmingly bad that sixteen dropped out. Eight desperate men, led by an unconquerable hero named L. K. Wood, struggled for forty days and nights through swollen streams, mud and snow, in broken mountain ranges as impenetrable as any wilderness in our land. Starved and dazed, they suddenly found themselves in a forest of frightening, giant trees. They thought those vast tree trunks were figments of a nightmare; that they had gone stark mad.

A few miles from the north end of San Francisco's Golden Gate Bridge, Muir Woods has the solemnity and hush of a cathedral. The tops of the trees are well below the surrounding ridges and, as you approach, the woods look dark and gloomy in contrast to the glare of the treeless mountainsides. Taking a steep path down to the floor of the forest, your eyes quickly adjust to a dim, delicious twilight. A redwood forest has more light in its depths than other conifer forests do. Compared to it the Douglas fir forest and the North Woods are black. The mighty columns are well spaced, with intervals between the trunks proportional to their diameters. The lowest branches of the canopies are a hundred feet above your head.

Sunshine, filtering through soft needle foliage, is diffused to a delicate light-green cathedral glow. Shafts of sunlight coming through openings in the canopy slant down as from high clerestory windows which tint them with colors. Where one of these shafts strikes a column, a patch of bark turns gold, and where a shaft hits the floor of the forest it catches sword ferns and wood sorrel in a bright green spotlight that glides slowly across the carpet like time through infinite space. In the redwood forest there is no clutter, no hurry. Everything is muted. A twig or cone from the faraway canopy falls silently into the sorrel. A footstep makes no sound. Here one instinctively—whispers. And no dog barks.

Even before men came, there were few animals in the dim hushed aisles of redwood forests. Only an occasional bear or deer wanders through on the way to a trout stream or a browse of twigs and berries. The giant condor, in his ceaseless winging, passes over these forests without diving.

An occasional squirrel silently clambers up-and-up-and-up to bite off a ripe cone and then stares downward, waiting a few seconds for it to reach the ground. Then he scampers down to pick up the seeds of the shattered cone—seemingly in slow motion because the squirrel is so tiny in comparison with his perpendicular highway.

Bulky big-tree sequoia's wider trunk and spreading canopy, also result from its particular location. Powerful sunlight curves over trees on high mountains in an arc of more than 180°. The trees respond by forming a broad dome. In the cirque of summits, snowy shoulders and gulf-like canyons, torrents from melting glaciers, dashing over rocks, carry rich solutions of minerals for the giant roots. But sediments are not as deep on a mountain as they are in a valley, so big-tree develops a horizontal root system, seldom penetrating the ground as much as eight feet. It is shallow anchorage for such an immense superstructure, but the root system of a single big-tree sequoia may occupy as much as three acres.

A relative of the sequoias demonstrates the survival capacities of conifers in an entirely different setting. Bald cypress (*Taxodium distichum*) forest prospers in warm, swampy areas from North Carolina to Florida and around bayous on the Gulf Coast. It lines estuaries and low shores of the Mississippi system as far north as southern Illinois. This sprawling forest is extensive but discontinuous, and the cypress swamps are interlarded with gum trees, magnolias, holly, live oak and loblolly pine.

Bald cypresses have the family legacy of long life and bigness. A few bald cypresses are alive today which were growing when the first white men came to America. This cannot be surely claimed for any other tree east of the Mississippi, although some white oaks, post oaks, and an old sassafras have been considered for the honor. The biggest dimension for bald cypress is reported to be 150 feet high, with a 12-foot trunk diameter above the bulge at the base. This dimension would be unimpressive in the company of sequoias or sugar pines, but the magnitude of bald cypress is greater than that of any other eastern tree.

Bald cypress cannot be defined by the traditional characteristics of other conifers on rocky mountain sides, glaring sand, or shallow acid soil. Leaving its sequoia kin three thousand miles away in the High Sierras and cool foggy valleys by the Pacific, bald cypress raised its forest on lowlands in the southeastern part of our country. Bald cypress spurned the sandy sun-dried stretches of that area, now well-furnished with slash and southern yellow pine, to put down its roots in fluid mud under deep swamp water.

With roots groping in unstable, virtually bottomless mud how can a tree erect a trunk a hundred or more feet in the air? Bald cypress wood is so heavy that a freshly cut log sinks in water. It would seem that the least sway of its ponderous column would easily rip its roots from the unstable mud and send it toppling. But *Taxodium* has achieved an outstanding feat of engineering. The base of the trunk flares out at the surface of the water. Where drought or drainage has lowered the water level of a cypress swamp, the bulbous base is seen to continue widening four or five feet below the surface. Bald cypress has the shape of a giant bottle with a long neck. This form tends to keep it in a vertical position, in the manner of a toy clown, weighted so that it cannot be tipped over.

The way the great base works can be seen when bald cypresses, undermined by floods, are carried downstream. Lodging on a sandbar they do not become barkless logs like other trees. When the water rises, they come upright again and put out leaves. However, the oldest biggest cypresses are not on river banks but in swamp forests where their canopies form a roof that stills the wind, and where for complete security root cables interlock down in the mud like a massive immovable anchor.

A great scientific enigma of bald cypress is—how can such a marvelous root structure grow and function without oxygen? The ground under other forests is permeated by air, while muck under the stagnant deep water of a cypress forest is notoriously lacking in oxygen. Such waterlogged soil is usually lethal to trees because living cells at tips of roots must have oxygen. Until recently, cypress knees were assumed to be the answer. These are erect projections that puncture the mirror of water at the base of bald cypresses. They are often mistaken for little stumps, and admired as fanciful bits of wood sculpture. These knees emerge from roots in deep water and their height varies to give them just the right length to project a foot or so above the average water level of the swamp. Botanists long supposed that this unique structure helped the roots to breathe by carrying oxygen down to them and carbon dioxide up. This made so much sense that the concept of cypress knees as aerators was widely accepted and there the matter rested until the Forestry Department at Duke University made some tests and obtained surprising results. They proved that there is no air and carbon dioxide exchange between cypress knees and roots. Moreover, the knees branch from upper roots, and those most deeply submerged, the ones which need oxygen most, do not erect knees.

Then what of the cypress knees? It is grasping straws to suppose that they are stabilizers to weight down roots. Although the knees are made of fine quality wood that never decays, they are hollow and light in weight. Their buoyancy would tend to lift a root in the water instead of weighting it down. Those huge interlocking cables that sink in water need no slight weights like these to steady them in unstable mud. Yet surely anything so prominent as a cypress knee is no mere caprice of nature.

I have a theory not gathered from any scientific report and unproved so far as I know, which might show the cypress knees to be especially wonderful. It also might explain another bald cypress enigma.

Bald cypress is one of the two American conifers that are not evergreen, that shed their leaves in winter like the broad-leaved trees of the deciduous forest. (The other is Tamarack up in the North Woods.) As we have noted earlier, the down-fall of leaves at the approach of winter, by halting a tree's respiration, conserves water in the wood during winter when below-freezing temperatures make the air dry. But there is no threat of dryness, no need to conserve water, where bald cypress grows. Bald cypresses are southern trees. An occasional freeze in the outside air would scarcely affect the moisture content in the steaming stillness of a cypress glade. This would seem to make needle-dropping in rhythm with winter a superfluous performance. But wait—needle-dropping makes the tree dormant, and this conifer must be dormant for a few months each year in order to survive. Let us see why.

Willow betrays the secret. Willow is one of the few deciduous trees which can flourish with roots in water-soaked soil where there is little or no oxygen. Almost all trees obtain the oxygen they need for root growing from air-filled spaces between soil grains. But recent experiments show that willow takes in oxygen through its twig tips and delivers it to root tips in drowned soil. This internal oxygen supply is limited, but sufficient for meagre root growing and to keep the root hairs of an established system operating. It is enough oxygen for willows, which do not have all of their roots permanently in water. They do not have massive root systems in silt under stagnant water like bald cypresses. The place of willows is beside ponds and streams, with some normal sunswept ground around their bases.

This leads to another surprising discovery—that the willow root system starts to grow near the base of the trunk when it is *triggered by light*. The botanical term for this is root primordia, microscopic knots of living cells on the trunk, earmarked to make roots. After these cells have been sparked by light, they swell, divide, bulge and elongate in night darkness until, thrusting into the ground, they elongate continuously in perpetual darkness.

This wonderful response to dark and light reflects an enzyme performance like that which makes seeds sprout. This parallel is underscored by the fact that the majority of seeds must be dormant for a time before they can be treated by light. So it is with root primordia. The tree must be dormant, not in leaf, for its trunkwood to sprout roots— and the root primordia must be struck by light.

On every hand nature duplicates phenomena of living cells. Until science produces contrary evidence, we can suppose that bald cypresses have an internal oxygen delivery system which works on a larger scale than that of the willows. And that those picturesque, lightweight knees puncturing the water among the trees are dispatching root-growing enzymes down to their roots in the black silt—but only when the bald cypresses are dormant with all their needles off!

The American bald cypress swamp forest is a magnificent mongrel with characters of the languorous tropical forest to the south and the brisk deciduous forest to the north. It is also a seething cauldron of life from top to bottom, unmatched by any other forest of our continent.

One of the arresting features of the bald cypress forest is the festoonery of Spanish moss,* a freakish escapee from tropical America that softens the angular lines of the cypress branches with long silver-grey garlands

* Not a true moss but a relative of pineapple, without roots and sap. The silver glint is from a down of hairs that absorbs water. An air plant, it uses the cypresses only for support and does not tap them for nourishment.

and swaying pendulums. The tropical style of the forest canopy—providing lofty perches for eagles, hawks, kites and osprey; Spanish moss for cover and nesting; smooth water landings for ducks and geese, and shallow places for long-legged waders—makes the bald cypress swamp forest America's busiest rendezvous for many races of birds. Here the most famous of American ornithologists have found their biggest adventure.

William Bartram, in 1772, was enchanted by flocks of Carolina parakeets, the only parrots native to the United States. He watched them "shell the balls" of the cypresses—tear apart the round cones to eat the seeds. The lovable clowns added bright iridescent greens and yellows and raucous cries to the cypress forest. The last lonely pair of parakeets was sighted in 1920.

Alexander Wilson, "the father of American ornithology," was thrilled and dazzled by an ivory-billed woodpecker he discovered in a cypress swamp in 1808. This is another wayfarer from the tropics with its home among the cypress trees. A few years after Wilson, James Audubon glimpsed ivory-billed woodpeckers among the cypresses in Louisiana and made his famous painting of these 24-inch birds with their gleaming round eyes and regal backswept red crests.

In 1942 Roger Tory Peterson struggled into the depths of the Singer Tract in Louisiana, its 80 thousand acres the last large area of virgin swamp forest, where he beheld with breathless excitement a pitiful pair of survivors of the bird known as the handsomest of all American forest birds. He heard the haunting call just before it whispered off into permanent silence—"an indescribable tooting note, musical, staccato, like the 'toy tin trumpet' of Alexander Wilson." One mateless female ivory-bill was seen in the Singer Tract as late as December 1946. After that, the power saw screamed through the trunks which had taken a thousand years to raise, and the ivory-bills that had come with the cypresses in an earlier age vanished with their trees. A study by the National Audubon Society has found that it took 6 square miles of virgin cypress swamp forest to support a single pair of ivory-bills.

Good facsimiles of those bygone cypress swamp forests remain. The ancient trunks were removed one by one,* leaving young cypresses and

* William Bartram wrote in 1765: "When the planters fell upon these mighty trees, they raised a stage around them to reach above the buttresses; on this stage eight or ten negroes ascend with their axes and fall to work around the trunk."

much of the island and water life intact. In localities where the old timber was taken more than a century ago, a new generation of cypresses pierces the water with its knees and long silver garlands sway from the branches. Today's cypress forest has a larger proportion of open ponds and swamps. It is still the outstanding rendezvous of many races of birds and its watery floor is a stewpot of bizarre life.

We have noted that it is the nature of conifer forests to locate in harsher areas where they have less competition. The mountain and hidden valley retreats of the big-tree and redwood sequoia relatives of bald cypress are a dramatic example of survival by isolation. The bald cypress —which evolved *before* the rise of the deciduous forest and brought flowering herbs, insects, bushes and pond plants—achieved a daring retreat. It developed a unique apparatus of buttress, root cables, knees and internal oxygen delivery by which it could raise a forest in fairly deep water and silt. In this setting, bald cypress seems to have accepted a harsher challenge than any other conifer. Today the bald cypress swamp is a teeming privacy.

The parrots and ivory-bills are gone, and the big soaring birds—bald eagle, osprey, black vulture, goshawk, and Everglade kite—which require large cypress forest territories are rarities. On the other hand, the population of colorful song birds and water birds converging on the cypress swamp forests at migration time may be greater than in Audubon's day.

Peterson saw more than 12 hundred wood ducks in five days and reports that "at sunrise the air rings with the chants of cardinals, Carolina wrens and titmice." Edwin Way Teale saw the flashes of gold and black when "a hundred goldfinches alighted in the cypresses." Another time, floating among the cypresses in a boat, Teale was "in the midst of a new and glorious experience . . . the whole cypress wood seemed full of prothonotary warblers." (These are named for the chief secretary of the Pope, who wears a brilliant orange-gold cape.)

The monarchs of this curious forest, elevated on their massive buttresses, are imperturbable and aloof from the ferment of life all around them. Similarly detached and silent, the protruding knees, snags and debris on the floor of the forest seem fixed in the water mirror, whose surface is ruffled by only occasional tiny events—the silent bursting of little black bubbles of methane gas which pop to the surface from decaying matter underneath, hurrying ripples from a fallen twig, the plop of a frog and little pinwheels of whirligig beetles acting like tiny outboards gone crazy. Their gyrations are supposed to scare off birds and frogs.

The water is continuous through the whole swamp, rising and falling with wet and dry seasons. Where it extends from the shadows into bright light, the surface is carpeted with acres of bright green, yellow, white, purple and red water plants—white and yellow pond lilies, golden club, water hyacinth, pickerelweed, frog's-bit, quillwort, bladderwort, iris, arrowhead, cattail, eelgrass and sedges.

Open canals run through this carpet, connecting countless ponds and lakes studded with islands that are piled up with tangles and clumps of deciduous forest. Older and larger areas of dry ground support high stands of oak, gum, sassafras, myrtle, and magnolia. Some of the larger islands, rich in luscious prey of birds, turtles, frogs and snakes, are magnets for animals from the deciduous forests to the north and have become the haunts of bear, otter, wildcat, deer, wolf, rabbit and opossum.

In more shallow water among the water plants, the coffee-colored water from under the cypresses mixes with the bluer sunlit water of the ponds to make a nourishing soup that supports myriads of water insect larvae. Here is found a fantastic chain of life.

If the larvae were not so tiny—most of them measure a fraction of an inch—and hidden under water, they would be known as the most ferocious and gluttonous animals on earth. They are powerful swimmers and frenzied killers. But they are better known in their adult form. After they acquire wings and break through the surface of the water, they are beetles, gnats, mosquitoes, caddis flies and dragonflies. Meanwhile these little underwater gangsters are not hidden from certain monsters which appear among them.

For example, here comes the hellbender, a salamander two feet long with a bloated ugly head, powerful wicked tail and lidless eyes the size of pinheads. Its body is wrinkled and flattened like a pad of mud. (The hellbender has an ancestor five feet long, whose skeleton was once mistaken for human.) He takes big gulps of insect larvae along with small fish, snails and crustacea.

The southern soft shell turtle is another tremendous eater in this area of the cypress swamp forest. Its flat round carapace eighteen inches across is a leathery hide rather than a shell. It rises like a patch of mud from the swamp bottom, extends a very long neck and laps up larvae with lightning jabs of its tongue.

Bufo americanus, the big cypress forest toad, squats in a spot of shade like a Buddha who sees all and knows all. Only one thing Bufo does not know—that a triangular black object in the grass is the head of a cottonmouth, watching the watcher. Bufo is collecting his dinner while squatting on his haunches without moving his head, while flies, ants, caterpillars, spiders, and other bits that come that way suddenly vanish. Bufo is using his long tongue like a lariat, whipping it out with invisible speed. Then cottonmouth yawns, his jaws flashing white. . . .

It would take a full second for pot-bellied Bufo to leap and disappear in the water, but in a small fraction of that time, after cottonmouth yawns, the toad finds himself traveling smoothly along the alimentary canal of the big snake. During the first part of this journey Bufo is not mutilated, and he may be quite comfortable in this warm, moist situation. If, before long, something startles the cottonmouth, the toad is the beneficiary of sudden regurgitation and goes hopping off to enjoy a splash after all.

Maybe the cottonmouth was startled by an alligator. In an undisturbed cypress forest this monster reaches sixteen feet. Since its lineage dates back to the Age of Reptiles it was probably an original native of the cypress forest. No forest animal ever stalked its prey with greater cunning. The alligator lies in wait, motionless for hours, the knobby eyes on the top of its head protruding like two knots on a semi-submerged log. The floating log trick enables the alligator to drift undetected close to a mudbank, while keeping its eyes fixed on the place where small animals, such as otters, opossums, rabbits and young wild pigs come down to the water to drink. Then it gives an explosive splash and a sudden lunge and knocks the prey senseless with its tail. The floating log idea is also rewarding offshore, where a wood duck bobbing on a pond, or a mallard dabbling among water lilies, suddenly disappears.

An arresting fact about a conifer forest in contrast to a deciduous forest is the passive role of the trees in the interplay of forest life. Bald cypresses are like other conifers in this respect, despite the luxurious fecundity of their swamp forest.

Exceptions are minor. The parakeets liked to eat bald cypress seeds, the ivory-bill lived on larvae bred in cypress wood which had been dead for exactly three years. The exceedingly slow decay of debris from the trees fell into water that is like black coffee, making a lurking place for the hellbender and cottonmouth. Cypress canopies modified wind, light and temperature, making the forest a pleasant retreat for caterpillars, birds and tree snakes; in the tall straight trees overlooking the ponds were wonderful perches and lookouts, but the sparse season foliage offers little cover or nest-building material without the Spanish moss.

The contributions of the cypresses to the total life of the forest are mostly structural; there is little reciprocity with the rest of the living scenery. The bald cypresses formed tall forests which stood in water before evolution embellished their home with pond lilies, birds, insects and animals that are mostly refugees from the deciduous forest. The cypress did not participate in this transformation.

In addition to the song birds, lush areas of this discontinuous forest are the homeland of America's most beautiful and dramatic fresh water birds. The snakebird (*Anhinga*) with a serpentine neck twelve inches long, can fly swiftly *under water,* darting this way and that to catch panic-stricken fishes. The neck shortens with coils that suddenly release, shooting the head forward. Then the head freezes and, with a kick of the feet and a flip of the wings held close to the body, the neck suddenly shortens again bringing the body and head together. The same spring action of the neck sends a sharp bill into the fish, like a harpoon.

The limpkin, whose ancestors go back 60 million years, was perhaps one of the first birds to arrive in the cypress swamp. Limpkin walks with dignity in shallow water, raising its feet high and putting them down so deftly that it does not muddy the water while looking for fresh water snails. Then with equal precision it uses its sharp bill like a nutpick, unwinding the snail from its shell.

The gallinule does not dive under water or fly in the air—having neither web feet nor proper wings. Its toes are four or five inches long; when spread its feet act like snowshoes enabling the bird to walk on pond lilies and water weeds. But with those attenuated toes it can also gather and grasp a bunch of vertical reeds. Using them like stilts, it hunts in the higher part of the reed jungle for butterflies and pollen, or any animal or vegetable dish that suits its mood.

Such are the true native birds of the bald cypress swamp forest. They evolved through millions of years with the rise of the deciduous forest and its herbs, flowers and insects. They are a beautiful example of the way each kind of forest wild life fits perfectly into its place. Here is a 4-

story pantry, well-stocked with different kinds of food, snails in the mud, fish in the water, insects on the surface, a miscellany up in the reeds—and a bird is designed exclusively to feed on each level.

The migrating waterfowl of the bald cypress swamp forest come splashing into the ponds in the fall, wave after wave—on schedule. In the spring—again on schedule—the flocks run on the water, pounding the surface with wet feet and striking it with wing tips that send up little spurts, then rise into the sky and vanish northward. No wild life of the American forest is better known than the ducks and geese—and is a greater mystery.

Bird migration is an ancient rite which has been traced back 80 million years in the fossil record. We are told that when the sun has been above the horizon for a certain number of hours and minutes on a day in late winter, the gonads of the birds are stimulated so that they leave a pond in the cypress forest for a pond in the North Woods or beyond among clumps of stunted birch, balsam and alder in the Arctic tundra. We are not concerned here with why they do it and how they navigate those thousands of miles, but will only note that they are a wonderful link between the bald cypress forests of our southland and the North Woods of Canada.

The Canada geese take off first. They migrate in family units. The families often get together and fly as one large flock. It is now known that they have fixed groups which travel together year after year and have their own resort colonies in the north. It is known that birds know each other as individuals, and probably the flock composed of a number of families has a sound and a sign language of its own.

One old adult who knows the way, points up the famous V formation and leads the honking. The travel speed of the V is around 40 miles an hour, which can be stepped up to 60 if need be. They could easily travel 500 miles a day and make the trip from the cypresses to the North Woods in two or three days, but the old ritual is curiously controlled. Canada geese in the vanguard of the spring migration are following an invisible line that runs across their path while it moves steadily ahead with the flow of spring. This line is drawn on the daily weather map, where it is called the 35°F. isotherm—it is a waving east-west contour representing an average temperature of 35 degrees, the *snow melt line*. By following it, the Canada geese will take three or four weeks to make the trip. When they arrive, there will be enough open water in the ponds of the North Woods for a safe landing, buds will be spilling out flowers and leaves, and fish and insects will be splashing and buzzing. Everything will be ready for them.

chapter fourteen

The North Woods

THE eastern front of the world's largest coniferous forest is a battlement of spruce spires on the brim of granite cliffs, with cold north Atlantic surf crashing at its base from Maine to Newfoundland. Behind this, stand legions of spires in eastern Quebec Province, from which a forest about 300 miles wide surges through the St. Lawrence watershed and then heads westward between the Great Lakes and Hudson's Bay.

Beyond Lake Superior the prodigious conifer forest—confronted by dry, high plains—curves due north and, widening, fills most of the area between Hudson's Bay and the Rocky Mountains. Here the green spires ring a series of beautiful midcontinental lakes—Winnipeg, Athabaska, Great Slave, Great Bear—as they continue northward 800 miles in the Mackenzie River watershed until clumps of trees stand within 30 miles of the shore of the Arctic Ocean.

In the far northwest, a lobe of this transcontinental forest extends into the valley of the upper Yukon and spills trees down into the low, rolling glacier-scarred land south of Mt. McKinley, where it forms millions of acres of the interior forest in Alaska. Here are the same kinds of spruces, balsam firs and tamaracks as those at the other end of the forest 4 thousand miles away in Labrador.

This is the North Woods, with medium-sized straight-trunked trees standing root to root. Even on small islands the spires crowd together so tightly that their silhouettes against the sky look like ships under full sail, painted on blue lakes. The North Woods, joined with the Mountain Forest on its western boundary and beyond that the West Coast Forest, constitutes the prime continuous coniferous forest on earth in respect to the number of square miles it covers and the density of its timber.*

Trim and erect white spruce, with lovely soft white wood and its foliage sugared with resin crystals, is the mainstay of the North Woods. Black spruce—picturesque, stocky, loaded with purple cones which cling for years—crowds cold bogs. Balsam fir and tamarack (larch) assemble in wetter, colder and more brightly lighted places. Northern white cedar (arborvitae) appears in swamps and on cool rocky ledges in southern areas of the North Woods. Red spruce substitutes for white spruce on the Atlantic frontier in Maine, and also represents the North Woods on the higher slopes of the White Mountains, Green Mountains, and Adirondacks. Thus, the conifers adapt to every situation imposed by the diverse geography of the North Woods.

White pine made superb masts and timbers for ship hulls and houses of the English colonists on the New England coast. But white pine is intermediate between the North Woods and the deciduous forest, where summers are longer and winters are less bitter.

The northern boundary of the North Woods undulates across the widest part of the continent as it adjusts to sunlight, water and cold winters. Here the forest is fragmented with clumps of stunted trees scattered on the tundra, and the North Woods fades where glaciers have very recently left the land and the ground under the tundra peat is permanently frozen.

Those stunted clumps are the advance guard of black spruce, balsam and tamarack, with the main body of white spruce close behind. The forest is still pressing northward in the wake of the glaciers, encompassing a million lakes and streams that form a glittering silver network in the North Woods. Spruce, balsam fir and tamarack are "modern" conifers but with ancient endowments for ancient, raw situations. The North

* The Siberian forest in Russia has more square miles with scattered Scotch pine and sizable patches of spruce and fir, but it is 30 percent deciduous and a large proportion is swampland, with stunted crooked trees (*taiga*), widely ravaged by fire. Most of the Siberian forest trees are not over fifty years old.

Woods conifers are so lusty, so indomitable that they have been able to raise this broad, beautiful forest almost instantaneously.*

The story of the outline and reach of the forest, with boundaries vividly defined by sea cliffs, large rivers, chains of lakes, and mountain ranges, is a thrilling one. It has been recently deciphered by radiometric methods for determining the age of rocks formed before the Cambrian period—more than 500 million years ago—at the beginning of the geologic calendar. The map of the North Woods is the map of the foundations of North America. This is the only area of North America continuously above ocean water since the continent was born—when an enormous mass of granite appeared, floating high among the molten materials of the earth's crust.**

For a billion years, while the granite was hardening, the pressures of heat and gas caused it to form a broad dome, an upheaval of granite which geologists call a shield. The Canadian Shield is one of the largest of these broad, symmetrical rock formations.

Its creation was accompanied by awesome pyrotechnics. The larger the shield grew, the greater was its weight and the more it pressed downward on the roiling volcanic magna in which the granite floated. The pressure caused doughy lavas of heavy minerals deep in the earth to ooze up around the edges of the shield, and in one area these volcanic forces split open a huge crack running from the southwestern edge of the shield due north for a thousand miles. Wherever the heavy mineral lava emerged, the granite of the shield became mixed with exceptionally large crystals of rare elements suc has uranius, zirconium, lead, gold. Usually these are buried deep under the sediments piled on continental land, in the hot depths of the crust.

Through timeless eras, the surface of the shield was worn down, but the Canadian Shield is so tremendous and had been uplifted so high that all of it stayed above the ocean, a continental nucleus of permanently dry land. However, in many places the uplift of mountains so weakened the

---

* Instantaneous in geologic time. The glaciers quit the Great Lakes around 8,000 B.C., where Indians saw them, and much more recently in northern parts of the forest.

** Granite is 50 percent oxygen and much lighter than volcanic rock, called basalt, which makes the floors of oceans, and underlies the high floating granite of North America.

Sharp spires of spruce in the North Woods, and on eastern mountain tops, shed snow which forms a genial blanket on the forest floor.

This mountain-climbing pine tree has snow white bark, survives terrific winds by growing horizontally.

The bare branches of this white oak make an artistic etching of the stricking symmetry and vigor of the tree.

shield that it gave way under the highest mountains, creating depressions for future lakes and river valleys.

The glaciers of the recent ice age made the latest assault on the shield. They ground off its projections, rounded its mountains, widened its valleys and flattened the broad convexity of the whole shield. Fragments of cracked rock, in the process of becoming rounded boulders, caught under the weight of ice, so abraded and disarranged the surface that when the glaciers melted the water ran into a crisscross of troughs and depressions. Thus was formed the silver network of streams and chains of lakes where the spruces unrolled their carpet of bristling spires.

The Canadian shield became the pedestal of the North Woods. Despite all splitting by intrusions of heavy plutonic minerals and the ravaging of its surface by glaciers, the shield which was the original North America is intact and tells the story of its fabulous past to the scientists of our time.

When the granite of the shield first appeared above water, shouldering off the primordial ocean like the back of a surfacing whale, volcanic forces underneath became concentrated in the center. This extra pressure, by stretching the fabric of the rock, weakened the structure of the central dome. In the recent ice age this highest part of the dome was the site of a great glacier, and the weight of the ice, pressing down where the granite was weaker, caused the plastic granite to sag—making a depression which became the basin of Hudson's Bay.

The chain of the Great Lakes—excluding Lake Superior—represents the site of an ancient mountain range on the southern border of the shield, and the Laurentian Mountains in Quebec are thought to be a residue of it. Around the edges, the structure of the shield is thinner and the upthrust along the southern border weakened it still more. The granite sagged and left shallow depressions that became river valleys—until these were gouged a bit deeper by later glaciers to form the basins of the Great Lakes.

Lake Superior, deeper than the others, marks the southern end of an even older and loftier mountain range, where the pressure of heavy mineral magna opened the great crack in the shield which has been mentioned that ran from the southwestern edge a thousand miles north. Lake Superior is thought to be the site of the highest mountain that ever existed on this continent, and the chain of beautiful big lakes to the north marks the site of unnamed and exceedingly high peaks whose weight depressed the basins of Lakes Winnipeg, Athabaska, Great Slave and Great Bear—all famous names in legends of the North Woods.

This explains why the area of Lake Superior and land farther north has outcroppings of plutonic rock in which men find large crystals of heavy elements like copper, nickel, lead, radium, iron and gold. Before white men came, Indians discovered the copper in the Lake Superior area. Geologists call this native copper; it is so pure that it can be used without smelting. This was the source of copper for Indian artifacts found scattered far and wide through the American wilderness.

The Lake Superior area is also the chief source of nickel in America, and the Mesabi Range—extending along the border of the shield west of Lake Superior into the North Woods of northwestern Minnesota—is famous for its iron ore. So pure is this ore that it could have come only from very great depths of the earth's crust.

Fifteen hundred miles to the northeast of the Mesabi Range, in a depth of the North Woods in Labrador little explored until today, equally pure iron ore has been discovered near the surface. In the far northwestern borders of the shield, Klondike gold in the upper Yukon valley has made American legends. Today, other important gold mining camps are established in the forest of northwestern Quebec and northern Ontario, where heavy minerals thrust through weaker borders of the shield.

This Canadian shield, embryo of the continent, whose weight as it grew larger forced the heavy mineral dough to ooze up around its edges and through cracks, and which was finally sculptured by glaciers, was the unique site of the great North Woods.

The magnitude of time condensed in the North Woods is awesome. The rocks under the spruces in the popular skiing areas of the Laurentian Mountains made dry land 1,100 million years ago, according to radiometric measuring. But the oldest land on the continent lies a thousand miles west of the Laurentians, among the spruces in the Lake of the Woods area, where the great split occurred in the shield when it was doming. Dry land rock formed there 2,500 million years ago!

The antiquity of the North Woods is dramatized by the Rocky Mountains, which lift their snowy peaks beyond the western edge of the Canadian shield. Here the legions of the spruces suddenly stop and a few lodgepole pines come down the eastern slopes of the Rockies to mingle in the fringes of the North Woods. Above them, majestic mountains that overlook the North Woods empire support an utterly different kind of forest.

It is a fantastic paradox that land now uplifted in the Rocky Mountains was under water as recently as 100 million years ago—yesterday in the career of the Canadian shield. The pedestal of the North Woods was in the open air and sunshine for more than 3 billion years before the ground which is now the Rocky Mountains showed above the sea. This is revealed by the discovery of sea shells and sharks' teeth in limestone a mile above sea level in the Rockies.

The Rocky Mountains have towering, snow-capped peaks, precipitous cliffs and roaring streams in deep canyons because they arose so recently that there has not been time for erosion to smooth them and wear them down, or for the mountains to subside because of crustal weakening. Those mountains beyond the western edge of the shield are counterparts of that far more ancient and loftier mountain range to the east that imprinted the series of beautiful spruce-lined lakes from Superior to Great Bear. But there was one important difference—there was no forest, no life whatsoever on the primordial mountains.

"The North Woods," has a personal ring. It hints of adventure in the unknown more than any other forest in North America, of the thrill of discovery.

The spell of the North Woods comes from an aura of remote strangeness. The shadows are blacker under the close-standing spruce than they are in other forests, and this creates a haunting sense of danger. No trails are found among the trees in the denser parts. The floor is a springy mattress of fallen needles that have piled up undecayed for years, underneath a deep carpet of dripping wet moss which undulates over fallen trunks like waves of dark green water. Everything is motionless. The silence is palpable, occasionally broken by the sudden, slight sounds of scratching and scampering where a marten is chasing a red squirrel in the tree branches.

In 1846, Thoreau left his green glades around Walden Pond for his first visit to what he called the backwoods of Maine. "There is no sauntering off to see the country," he wrote, "and ten or fifteen rods seems a great way from your companions, and you come back with the air of a much-traveled man as from a long journey with adventures to relate though you may have heard the crackling of the fire all the while—and at a hundred rods you might be lost past recovery·and have to camp out. It is all mossy . . . the trees are standing night, and every fir and spruce you fell is a plume plucked from the night's raven wing."

Here was a different kind of forest where men found no place to ride a horse, no ground to plow, no meadow for a horse or cow to graze. The motionless spires have an air of a forever forest, firmly fixed in place. Boundlessness in every direction contributes much to the spell of this paradise of hunters, traders and trappers. There is always another unexplored corner, always another lake or unnamed stream.*

The Canadian North Woods are trackless in contrast to trodden ground connecting distant areas of the forest, which in other American forests were made by animals and Indians. The silver netting of streams studded with blue lakes left by the glaciers constitute the finest forest trails in the world, and they run in every direction. The silver netting is also a superb irrigation system. It traps the rain and snow that falls upon 2 million square miles of North Woods, stores it in pure deep lakes and delivers it to every locality. With this network of water, the North Woods suffers no drought, no widespread forest fires. Burns are insignificant in the main body of the forest on the Canadian Shield, and where they occur locally the scars are quickly healed by new growth.

The greatest forest fires of American history have hit forests with a high percentage of spruce, pine and fir in areas exposed to dry winds on mountain sides, or where relative humidity drops below 30 percent due to the destruction of trees by logging and road building. The famous Tillamook Burn of 1933 was started when the friction of a lumberjack's chain struck sparks while dragging a log. The fire spread swiftly and destroyed 355,000 acres of the finest stand of Douglas fir in the Coast Range of Oregon. The worst forest fire of American history started near Green Bay, Wisconsin, in October 1871 (by coincidence, on the same night that Mrs. O'Leary's cow kicked over a stable lantern that started the great Chicago Fire). This raged over more than a million acres of

---

* To this day many people have never heard of Grand Falls, the biggest waterfall of the continent in interior Labrador—85 feet higher than Niagara and with a much greater head of water—that has cut in granite a canyon 10 miles long with walls up to 900 feet high. This has been named Bowdoin Canyon in honor of two Bowdoin College boys named Cary and Cole, who in 1891 found it, and then with dogged courage staggered back through the forest to tell their story. They had managed to sustain themselves for a month after losing their supplies and equipment in an upturned canoe.

the finest virgin white pine, destroyed the lumber center of Peshtigo and other towns and killed about 1,500 people.

The biggest fire—in point of the number of trees destroyed—occurred in the spring of 1910 in the Idaho panhandle. Three million acres of prime forest in the Bitteroot and Coeur d'Alene ranges of the Rocky Mountains were destroyed, including many towns, and 78 fire fighters were killed. The only thing that stopped that fire was a downpour of rain and a snowstorm.

The North Woods water network has made possible a vast mature forest of conifers highly charged with incandescent resin. Resin promotes radiant health in the North Woods by repelling the bacteria and fungi of decay, and insects, all of which find it distasteful. The North Woods would be utterly different and unrecognizable without its silver netting; in fact, it would not be our North Woods at all. Conifers, equipped to cope with the aridity of the winter freeze in that latitude, might have invaded the glittering granite empire without its many lakes, but the trees would have formed separate patches of small forest where sediments had accumulated in broad depressions. The trees themselves would have been sparse and wind-twisted like trees on a high mountain. They would not have had that juicy, deep, wall-to-wall carpeting of north-woods moss. Their trunks would not have been upthrusting spear shafts crowded together. Such a forest would not have been pervaded by the black shadows that hold the peculiar mystery which extends on and on across the continent. That hypothetical forest, without the sweep of fishes, birds and animals of ponds and marshes, would possess an appalling calm as if awaiting future creation.

The ponds and lakes have full exposure to sunlight; some are so large that they make horizons of blue water. The many thousands of miles of shoreline are characterized by fertile banks, sandy beaches and coves— fringed with many hardy trees and flowers from the deciduous forest. Shelves and boulders of sun-warmed rocks are carpeted with mosses, lichens and ferns where, as Kipling expressed it, "a man may bask and dream to the click of shod canoe poles, 'round the bend." Shallow marshes support immense thickets of heath, weighted in season with crowberries, bearberries and blueberries.

The life energy, sealed in the North Woods by winter cold, is released suddenly in the spring. In the deciduous forest, spring's arrival is gentle and deliberate, requiring a few months for fulfillment. But in the North

Woods spring is triggered by a sunrise. By the end of March it is day-light before five in the morning and until after seven in the evening. The temperature falls below freezing each night, but tops 80°F. in the sun. The snow drifts, which seemed so deep and enduring a few weeks ago, are melting fast. Then comes a frost-free night, and another; water is running on every hand. This is the signal. Trees and bushes are suddenly flushed with green. Regiments of blue lupine, purple fireweed and yel-low poppies unfurl their banners, and a myriad of tiny red and white bells dangle on the heath bushes. Spring swoops suddenly upon the North Woods, ruffling the lakes and ponds, speeding the pace of streams, diving into the marshes on the wings of millions of beautiful birds.

The birds had heard the explosion of spring in the North Woods when they were in faraway places—around the Gulf of Mexico, in the West Indies, in South America, in California, North Carolina, Virginia, New Jersey. Some birds heard it in Gibraltar, Italy, the Azores. Still others heard it while at sea in the Humboldt Current off Peru and Chile. Now, from around the world, they converge on the Canadian shield and hit the targets of their home spots scattered across 3 million square miles.

The muzzles of moose cut sliding V's on the mirrors of the ponds, on their way to the marshes and the browse of fresh aspen leaves. Beavers appear from their twiggy constructions in the ponds and set to work, vigorously felling aspens to dam a stream. She-bears leave their dens under fallen trees and stumble along the banks of streams, each followed by a pair of comical cubs, while mother covetously eyes the trout-laden water. Aristocratic members of the weasel family—Canadian sable, ermine, fisher and mink—scramble up tree trunks to chase squirrels and each other in the branches.

These are some of the events in the chain reaction set off by the ex-plosion of spring amid running waters and standing spruces. A man who travels the trails here finds them as pristine as the untouched woods—canoes do not leave a trodden trail, nor do snowshoes. A person has a sense of being the first arrival. He breathes the pure air, hears the splash of fish and a bird's song, and sees the play of blue tints in sky and water. The forest seems to belong to him and his heart responds with joy.

Any number of choices are offered for an overnight stop. You can pitch your tent and make your campfire on the bank of a river, the beach of a lake, on a little island, among white birches on a promontory, or in a clearing among trees near a stream. The hospitality of the North Woods is as reliable for a man as for an animal. With a canoe you can go anywhere and be self-sustaining—if you know the ways of the wilderness.

Samuel Hearn, who explored the area from the St. Lawrence River to Hudson's Bay for the Hudson's Bay Company in 1770, tells about finding a white woman who had escaped into the forest after having been taken prisoner by a band of Indians. She had neither canoe nor gun, and she had not seen a human face for seven months. There was plenty of water to drink, some berries in season, but she had lived chiefly by snaring small game such as partridges, rabbits and squirrels.

It is wonderful to realize that such a place still exists. The North Woods from Indian times to this day has been canoe country; it is the forest emblem of America more than other conifer forests of this continent, although others we have mentioned may be world-famous spectacles. It is more the forest emblem of America than the beautiful deciduous forest. No other continent has a North Woods.

The great forest on the Canadian shield must be canoe country, or snowshoe country, and nothing else. Or the North Woods will lose its essence and die. Today, bulldozers can fell trees a hundred times faster than men with axes. Logging and iron-mine railroads are cutting up the silver netting. Outboards are rending the peace and quiet of the lakes— frightening the long-legged moose and the long-legged birds that are retreating and disappearing, never to be seen again. Highways are bringing an influx of intruders and shooters who would only tip over a canoe.

chapter fifteen

A Man and a Wilderness

INCREDIBLE as it may seem the highest mountains of our continent bounding the whole western side of the North Woods, were unseen and unknown to the dauntless men in the fur country for two centuries. The snow-capped peaks, profound canyons and valleys were the stronghold of a giant forest. Its character is revealed by the way this wilderness resisted exploration until almost the nineteenth century.

Toward the end of the eighteenth century, one man cleft the harshest recesses of this wilderness. Alexander Mackenzie, cool eccentric wilderness demigod, performed virtually single-handed two towering exploits. Actually they were but one exploit, for the astounding 3-thousand-mile round-trip journey on the Mackenzie River in 1789 was only a dress rehearsal for the 1793 conquest of the most forbidding region of the continent—the region where the Rocky Mountains and coast ranges raise a series of impassable barriers between the canoe country and the Pacific Coast. A decade after Mackenzie's feat, the historic Lewis and Clark Expedition, hailed as the first crossing of the continent, won one of the biggest headlines of American History.

Mackenzie was knighted for enlarging the Empire, yet because he discovered no northwest passage, even for a canoe, he all but faded from history. Today the Mackenzie River is truly a magnificent monument

217

to the man, but one not fully appreciated. The main stream of the Mackenzie River has a greater mileage than the main stream of the Mississippi, and the tremendous Mackenzie watershed has far greater drama
and beauty of lake and forest than the Mississippi. It links three vast
lakes with some 30 thousand square miles of blue water.

Mackenzie's first exploit was a mistake, or so he thought—an outlandish voyage to the Arctic Ocean in a birchbark canoe—which left him
frustrated and chagrined. He called the mighty river which now bears his
name The River of Disappointment.

Mackenzie returned to Fort Chipewyan on Lake Athabaska with his
mind made up. He set forth without delay on another canoe trip through
the lakes, streams and portages of the North Woods back to Montreal.
There he embarked on the long trans-Atlantic voyage to London, where
social circles were buzzing with tales from the boundless American forest,
and commercial circles were avid for news of the fur trade. But laconic
Mackenzie shunned social invitations and kept to himself while he studied
astronomy and learned how to take bearings with a sea captain's instruments. After the winter in London, Mackenzie set forth for his headquarters at Fort Chipewyan with a small telescope, quadrant and time-
piece in his luggage.

For two years he pursued his job as Indian trader and sent valuable
canoeloads and sledgeloads back to his partners in Montreal. But beyond
the sunset, not too far away, was the Pacific Coast. The longitude of the
coast was known from surveys made fifteen years before by Captain
James Cook. And current reports reaching Mackenzie via London and
Montreal, about labyrinths of seaways among forested islands, intensified
his resolve to paddle and portage from Fort Chipewyan to the Pacific
Coast.

Mackenzie planned his canoe trip to the Pacific Ocean according to
the paddle-portage tradition of the North Woods. Each spring, as soon
as the ice went out, oversized canoes loaded with handsome pelts left
far-flung trading post forts on voyages to depots around the Great Lakes,
trips which might be upward of 500 miles and take weeks. The party
comprised six or eight French paddlemen, perhaps one or two travelers
and a representative of the fur company who was in charge and made
all the decisions with the authority of the captain of a ship.

In North Woods terms, this was a "brigade." It was designed for
far, fast travel, to avoid ambushes by hostile Indians, or fur bandits.

The brigade was provisioned for minimum hunting and cooking and the schedule called for the least possible delays in camping and resting.

Shortly after sunrise on May 9, 1793, ten men quit a log cabin on the banks of an unknown river, stepped into a big canoe and headed upstream against its massive flow.

Mackenzie had assembled his team during the two years at Fort Chipewyan after his return from London. The brigade consisted of six seasoned French-Canadian paddlemen, called *les voyageurs des bois,* two young Indians and a Mr. Alexander MacKay.

Of course, Mackenzie would expect to be confronted by lonely, dangerous wilderness, but he could have no idea of the succession of glacier-topped mountain ranges, steep trackless forest, raging rivers, canyons, cataracts and torturing mileages. At that time no European had seen the northern Rocky Mountains. If Mackenzie heard any rumors about mountains and tumultuous streams from Indians, he might have visualized mountains like the Laurentians or the Scotch highlands. He would expect troublesome portages around rapids and waterfalls or through thickets and swamps to get the canoe to another lake or stream where they could paddle in the right direction. His crew of hardened professionals could cope with such situations. So the first crossing of the Rocky Mountains was organized as a canoe trip similar to the long distance expeditions of the fur companies.

Our maps tell us that the river on which those ten men embarked that May morning in 1793 is the Peace River, a unique river in two ways. It is the only river on the continent that cuts straight through a major range of the Rockies at right angles. And it has no source in any lake or brook up in the mountains. The Peace begins suddenly where two large rivers collide head-on in an interior Rocky Mountain valley surrounded by snowy ridges and glaciated heights. It thunders into a dark, deep canyon through the mountain range, rushes down through the foothills and meanders across a western plateau of the North Woods to deposit its massive flow into Lake Athabaska after a course of nearly 700 miles.

In preparation for the second try to paddle to the Pacific Ocean, Mackenzie, in the autumn of 1792, moved his hand-picked brigade about 150 miles from Fort Chipewyan up the Peace River where they built a small fortress in which to spend the winter. Here they were dependent upon their own companionship and resources for six months.* Mackenzie was grimly determined to reach the Pacific Coast this time, so he forced his party to live together through a long, lonely, bitter winter, away from the diversions and contacts of a trading post, while he studied each man.

They built a superb canoe—25 feet long inboard, 4 feet 9 inches beam, 26 inches depth of hold. Birchbark sheathing is tough and flexible and so lightweight that even a great canoe can be carried easily on long portages. As in French canoes, a long narrow board ran from stem to stern to protect the bottom when scraping across gravel and rocks. Each of *les voyageurs des bois,* in addition to his paddle, had a 10-foot iron-shod pole. A 420-foot towline was included in their equipment.

Mackenzie's report notes that they embarked with a deadweight cargo of 3 thousand pounds, which included a ton of food for three months. He planned to supplement their fare with game, but he also wanted to push ahead with the least possible delay for hunting. They loaded sixteen 90-pound bags of pemmican (cakes of chopped moosemeat mixed with fat, crushed berries and fruits and dried), 600 pounds of corn, flour, rice and sugar and a ration of one fifth of a pint of rum per man per day. The rest of the cargo, exactly 100 pounds per man, consisted of arms, ammunition, presents for Indians, a miscellany of cooking utensils and canoe-building tools, axes, a tent for Mackenzie, his astronomical instruments from London, a brace of pistols, a sword, moose hides cured for making moccasins and a parcel of vermilion.**

They were off to a glorious start that morning in early May. The ground was still white with snow in the denser clumps of trees, but the snow patches were not deep and silent like winter snow, they seemed to be creeping, spawning puddles and coming alive in gurgling brooks. After the first day the sky was suddenly much wider and brighter and the red glow of sunsets lay upon the river. The tall forest shrank away where smaller trees in scattered clumps alternated with blue ponds and cattail bogs. Instead of dark forest lining the banks of every lake and

* A decade later, down on the Mississippi River, Lewis and Clark prepared for their fabulous expedition through the unexplored Rockies in the same way—they isolated the members of their expedition for six months in a wilderness encampment to condition them for a grueling effort.

** Vermilion is a stable red pigment, obtained by pulverizing a rock called cinnabar. Man has used it since the dawn of civilization; the red pictures in ancient Egyptian tombs were painted with it. We shall see how it served Mackenzie.

Superb conifers found in no other region on earth are assembled in a mountain setting at Santa Barbara, California.

Dark forests of mountain hemlock a mile above sea level on cliffs surrounding fabulous Crater Lake, Oregon.

Bright light and mineral sands of the Southeast coastal plains produce a widespread, open forest of tall pines.

stream, the land here was a playground for the winds, with open spaces for sunlight to slide across.

Every spot burgeoned with fresh spring life. A shadowy moose in an alder thicket stopped munching twigs bursting with buds and grunted querulously at the strange sight of a canoeful of men. A she-grizzly waded into the river up to her knees where a school of fish was splashing, to dish up the springtime delicacies for two cubs whining on the bank. She stared incredulously at the canoe, then wheeled, splashed out of the river and galloped away, the cubs bobbing along behind. The mirror of a pond was suddenly ruffled by a flock of migrating birds which had dropped out of the sky. It was the time just after the snow cover had melted from the bearberries, when the soggy muskeg teemed with larvae, mice and lemmings; and the long-distance bird migrators were flying across thousands of miles to this, their ancestral breeding ground.

Mackenzie's party may have seen hundreds of magnificent whooping cranes traveling through the air with long necks extended. (The whooping crane is America's tallest bird, standing five feet high; it is immaculately white with bright red naked patches on its cheeks and legs.)

Everyone reacts to scenery according to his nature and way of life. The ranchman loves the prairie, the mariner the sea, mountain men the lofty peaks, and fur traders lakes and streams with an abundance of game. Thus the imperturbable Mackenzie recorded rare delight that first week on the Peace, with fine canoeing and pageants of game: "A succession of the most beautiful scenery I have ever beheld."

They were paddling across a unique area, the broad threshold of the Mountain Forest, which geologists have labeled the Peace River Block. A big section of the Canadian shield was cracked off, slightly uplifted and tilted by the same forces that pushed up the Rocky Mountains which abut its western edge. Due to the mildness of winter snows to leeward of the mountains and to the drainage from the tilting, the tall dark spruce forest encroaches very little upon the 40 thousand square miles of this platform. It is a scene of low river banks, scattered forest of black spruce, larch and aspen, unending vistas of alder, willow and birch thickets, and extensive bulrush and cattail bogs. The combination of exposure to the open sky, shallow waters and wading areas, thickets for small game cover and groves of trees for large game cover, makes the Peace River Block a magnificent breeding ground and sanctuary for wild life.

As Mackenzie's canoe followed the serpentine course of the Peace River westward, the land gradually became higher and drier. The groves of North Woods spruce, larch and balsam fir were left behind. Ponds and bogs were replaced by rolling prairie. "Abundance of game" was noted by Mackenzie, but he had not gone there to list the wild life. He and his men were possessed with the single thought of paddling as far and as fast each day as possible. They must have seen pronghorn antelope and coyote, and perhaps some wolves. When they made camp just before sunset little cottontail rabbits, pocket gophers, deer mice and ground squirrels would have been peeking out of holes or running around in a panic.

Mackenzie's six solemn *voyageurs* wielded their paddles with tireless rhythm and pushed the big heavily laden canoe against the powerful current of the Peace River for fifteen hours a day. In that latitude, midspring days are long, the hours of darkness short. Their schedule called for landing at seven, a couple of hours of daylight game hunting for the two Indians, a hearty dinner and five hours of sleep. They were up at sunrise around 2 A.M., had breakfast, loaded the dunnage and then embarked for another fifteen hours during which few words were spoken and a hypnotic silence was broken only by the pulsebeat of the paddles.

In eight days Mackenzie and his men had crossed the Peace River Block, having paddled some 300 miles. In the second week they made only 150 miles against faster water that steadily lifted the canoe into hilly country where the land was eroded with stony benches and there were few lakes and streams. They had rounded a bend and were headed southward. Scattered forests had reappeared on higher slopes in the form of sharp vertical spruce and lodgepole pines that seemed to cast no shadows, and the undergrowth was sparse. On their right hand to the west they saw range after range of blue hills, stepping higher and higher to a background parade of colossal mountains that merged their snowfields with the sky. The spectral ridges ran as far as the eye could see, northward and southward, without a gap that might mean a river valley or offer a portage. The Pacific Ocean was on the far side of those seemingly endless mountain ranges. There was no promise of a water passage through the montains, and here they were in a fine canoe with a ton of equipment, with no choice but to paddle southbound up the river.

The Mackenzie brigade had left behind them the familiar North Woods country, and were now confronted with stupendous mountains—a blank on their maps. This was a situation for which Alexander Mackenzie was not prepared. To this day no craft has ever navigated the savage Peace River Canyon. At the canyon entrance, the Peace is only 35 feet wide, but with unplumbed depths. The volume of three big rivers are combined here to rampage through a constricted outlet with a thunder that shakes the cliffs that tower 300 to 700 feet on either side.

When Mackenzie arrived in late spring, the roaring chute in the Peace River Canyon would have been swollen by melting glaciers and snow and the surface would have been surging like storm waves in mid-Atlantic. Today a 20-mile portage trail winds above the cliffs to the upper end of the canyon.

Mackenzie, however, did not know the length of the canyon, and better water might be just around the bend. With a 25-foot canoe loaded with all their supplies, he decided not to portage but to force a way up through eddies and shallows at the base of the canyon walls. But he quickly surrendered when he realized, as he noted in his log, that "The river as far as we could see was one whitesheet of foaming water."

To surmount those mountainous cliffs called for an appalling portage, but a portage nevertheless—something they understood and were ready to tackle. Mackenzie ordered *les voyageurs* to haul the cargo up a coulee. They cut their way through the forest and had the luck to come upon an Indian portage trail. A repeat trip, and the canoe was carried through the conifers to the head of the canyon. Mackenzie, peering down at swirling waters hundreds of feet below, noted with amazement "natural cylinders" in the rock ledges at the base of the cliffs.*

Beyond the canyon the brigade made their first use of the canoe repair materials they had brought. Birchbark can take a lot of punishment, but the big canoe had been badly damaged in the attempt to mount the canyon and on the rugged haul over the ridge. They had achieved an almost superhuman feat in getting their outfit across this 20-mile portage, but in Mackenzie's log, nobody is tired and nobody is praised.

Back in the canoe, everything was fine. They were still headed due west and the water in the river was undiminished. But, to their bewilderment, it seemed to flow directly out from under another mountain range a few miles ahead, this one much higher, with snow-capped peaks. The fabulous Peace River Canyon had only cut through a foothill range and they were now confronted with a major range of the Rockies.

The Peace comes through the major range in a gap with sloping sides. Men in recent years have shot the rapids as a daredevil stunt, but only

* Two explorers who went through there in the 1950's found the primeval canyon unmarked by trails and just as Mackenzie had left it 160 years before. They too marveled at the huge, spiraling potholes where the rocks had been reamed by whirlpools.

at lower water in late summer. Mackenzie's men tried to buck the current without portaging. They paddled, poled and frogged * their big canoe up through the eddies under the cliffs, where a rush of water that nothing could stem ran in the center of the river. It was the old game of "catching the eddy"; if they missed, the canoe would be torn from their clutches, swept backward and shattered against the rocks. In one place they had to cut steps in solid rock high on the face of a cliff to get a foothold on a ledge a few inches wide, so that they could drag the canoe (far below them at the end of 360 feet of towline) through whirlpools too deep for poling. They were still headed westward. If they could only get the canoe through this range. . . .

On the 21st day from their starting place, with 400 miles of the massive flow of the Peace behind them, the great river came to an abrupt end. They beheld a steep slope bearing a forest of spruce with cottonwood at the water's edge, directly across the bow of the canoe. A few miles beyond the precipitous flank they saw another tremendous mountain range towering above the treetops. A good-sized river at right angles to the Peace flowed along the base of the forest slope from the north, and another river, also at right angles to the Peace, flowed along the base of the same ridge from the south. Weirdly, the two rivers had their mouths in the same spot where they met, and their collision produced the source of the Peace River.

On our maps the river flowing into the Peace River from the north is called the Finlay, and the one coming in from the south is called the Parsnip. The Finlay is twice as long as the Parsnip; moreover it trends westward to its source in three lakes only about 135 miles from the head of a Pacific Ocean fjord. The sinuous Parsnip measures only a little more than a hundred miles before it peters out. But it should be easy for experts without maps to choose the best waterway for working a 25-foot canoe upstream by merely looking at the mouth of the two rivers. And so it was. *Les voyageurs* found their voices. They earnestly urged turning north instead of bucking the shallower white water southward. As we might put it, they had "had it."

Mackenzie, against the opposition of all the others, ordered the turn southward up the Parsnip. Why? Mackenzie could witness as well as the others the deeper, easier water to the right, and the faster, noisier water

* Everybody goes overboard and taking firm hold of the gunwale they walk the canoe upstream among the rocks while wading up to the waist.

to the left. It is rumored that Mackenzie, during the winter in the Athabaska area, consulted a very old Indian who said that he had been far beyond the sunset in his youth. The old Indian scratched a T in the sand, and indicated that if Mackenzie turned left at the top of the T, Indians near the head of the river would show him a portage westward over the range to a river *flowing to the sea*.

Fur traders had strong reservations about Indian accuracy with respect to distances, all the more so when talking about country outside their tribal territories. So, if the old Indian story is true, Mackenzie had kept the advice to himself—until at the top of the Peace he saw what the old Indian was talking about. He may also have had a bias for a turn southward after the frustration of the northward trip on the River of Disappointment.

For twelve days they paddled, poled and frogged, fighting their way up the mountain-tight valley of the Parsnip River to its source in a small lake. This in itself was a tremendous, unsung feat of this incredible man. At the source of the Parsnip he stood at the remote and ultimate source of the great Mackenzie River system, having canoed its entire length of 2,420 miles from the delta on the Arctic Ocean to this faraway spot in the interior of the highest Rockies.

He was looking about for a portage westward when two Indians turned up, utterly astonished by their first sight of white men. In return for priceless bits of colored cloth and trinkets, they led the Mackenzie brigade, still toting their great canoe and supplies, on a portage westward over a high pass through the mountains. Here, at long last, they crossed the Continental Divide.

After three days of brutal portaging, they launched their canoe in a tumbling, rushing stream that was going their way, and went plunging down the western slope toward a fine winding river in a broad valley. But they were coasting too fast. It is safer to frog and line a canoe upstream in turbulent water, than to be hurled downstream among boulders and drift piles of fallen trunks. The greatest canoe ever built in the North Woods was totally wrecked in the midst of the dark forest of enormous conifers before they reached the valley floor. Mackenzie labeled it "Bad River" on his chart. Without resting, the men gathered their belongings from the wreckage and packed them through pristine forest down to the valley. In four days they built a new canoe.

The brigade now was headed westward on a generous, winding river, going with the current. With a 50-mile bend, the fine winding river in the valley rounded a heavily forested highland, called the Caribou Mountains, an area of 12 thousand square miles that is still blank on our maps.

A gratified Mackenzie was sure they had reached the Columbia's River. When he was in London studying navigation in the winter of 1792-93, Fleet Street was buzzing with reports from Captain Robert Gray of the sloop *Columbia* about a navigable waterway coming out of the heart of the Coast Forest. Mackenzie did not live to correct the mistake he had made. He was not on the Columbia's River, but on the Fraser River, a dramatic trunk waterway of the central valley of the Rockies. In the full glory of June, the Mackenzie brigade was passing through a pristine mountain wilderness, loaded with wild life and watered by torrents from melting glaciers and snow-filled ravines.

On their third day of paddling southward on the Fraser River, they passed the mouth of a sizable stream coming out of the mountains to the west, and sixty miles farther they suddenly beheld a tribe of excited Indians and a big lodge. Mackenzie had seen nothing like that lodge in the North Woods. He betrayed his astonishment by the way he describes its details in his log. This was no wigwam, but a permanent structure built with large tree trunks, mortised together. The interior measured 30 by 40 feet, and it had three fireplaces, rows of twig beds, shelves for dried fish and some cleverly designed salmon traps were stored in a corner.

The Indians, isolated in the heart of the mountains, had never seen white men, although reports about pale-faces who had visited the coast in "large canoes" had come over the mountains into the Fraser Valley. This was the first historical encounter of a white man with a Rocky Mountain Indian tribe. The Fraser River valley was at the eastern end of a trade route crossed once a year in the spring, when the Indians bartered from tribe to tribe between the interior valley and the coast. When explorers Bering, Cook, Vancouver and Gray were on the coast, some 85 thousand Indians in about 50 tribal groups lived in the area that is now British Columbia.

Probably the ancestors of the Fraser Valley Indians, migrating from the coast, had brought the skills for building the great tribal lodge. The abundance of game in the valley, particularly moose, brought affluence to the Fraser River Indians. Unheard of in the rest of the world, these tribes in the heart of the Mountain Forest were beneficiaries of the world-wide trade of European countries in the late eighteenth century.

We can see on our maps that Mackenzie might have continued down the Fraser and that, in the course of 350 miles, the river would have delivered him to the sea where the city of Vancouver stands today. But Mackenzie could get no information about where the river would take them. The ancestors of the Fraser Valley Indians had come across the mountains, their trade and the seacoast were toward the west. Lands to the south were unknown and occupied by hostile tribes. For several days Mackenzie's party exchanged gifts and food and made earnest inquiries. They hated mountains, and now they were canoeing downhill. We do not know whether the two Indians from Athabaska were any help with the strange dialect, but this did not matter where men conversed by gesticulating and scratching in the sand.

The Indians insisted that they must go back upstream to the river which they had noted flowing from the west, and follow that on foot. Up in the mountains they would come to a trail that would lead them down the west slopes to a friendly tribe, the Bella Coolas, who would take them to salt water. The river out of the west was dangerous white water and they should not try to get their canoe up it.

So Mackenzie ordered his brigade to turn around and paddle upstream, retracing about 60 miles on the Fraser to reach the mouth of the tumultuous river they had passed. (On our maps it is named West Road River.) He had been told by the number of suns, counted on the fingers of both hands, that this was the end of their canoe trip. It would be a long trek with no portage. Mackenzie said he was going to back-pack and go it alone, and that the others could camp in this place where game was abundant and await his return. Whereupon every man volunteered to go with him.

They cached the canoe and heavy supplies, back-packed all they could carry and trekked in single file. The two Scotsmen were in front to cut trail and watch for wild animals and savages; the others stumbled along after them through dense forests, over fallen timbers and icy creeks. *Les voyageurs des bois* carried 90 pounds, the Indians 45 pounds of supplies.

Mackenzie drove hard on the sunrise-to-sunset schedule. To save time he forbade hunting and said they must live on the pemmican and rum in their packs. "It was determined that we should content ourselves with two meals a day, which were regulated without difficulty as our provisions did not require the ceremony of cooking."

The Fraser Valley Indians, who made one round trip a year, left no path. The trail was simply keeping in touch with the river on one side or the other. Thus, the brigade, averaging less than a mile an hour, put 90 miles of wilderness behind them.

A Canadian government surveyor, F. C. Swannell, reports in the Hudson's Bay Company magazine *Beaver* (1958) about his visit to the area. "There was never so wild and lonely a mountain passage as that traversed by Alexander Mackenzie's brigade in 1793." It is an anarchy of peaks, one a volcanic cone 8,130 feet high, with sheer cliffs of vividly red and yellow basaltic rock, where Mackenzie crossed around the shoulder. Twenty miles west another massive peak 8,100 feet was ringed with hanging glaciers. Mr. Swannell identified a ridge of craggy peaks 8,500 feet high, which Mackenzie saw when they were descending desperately steep slopes. Mackenzie noted: "Before us appeared a stupendous mountain whose snow-clad summit was lost in the clouds. As we proceeded, the mountains appeared to withdraw from us. The country between them soon opened to our view, which apparently added to their awful elevation." This has a ring of elation—they were descending to sea level.

They were indeed on the home stretch. About ten miles beyond the source of the river which had guided them from the Fraser to the heights, they had come upon a lodge of Ulkatchos,* a tribe of Carrier Indians. Here was an Indian culture such as they had never dreamed of. This lodge was even more elaborate than that of the Indians on the Fraser. "The timber was squared on two sides, and the bark taken off the two others, the ridgepole extending about 8 or 10 feet beyond the gable end and supporting a shed over the door. The end of the ridgebeam was carved as a snake's head. Hieroglyphics of similar workmanship painted with red earth decorated the interior of the building."

The tribes who lived among those peaks of the Coast Forest and whose moccasin trails across precipitous slopes and through dark forests converged at the head of the Bella Coola River are called Carrier Indians, because they are usually seen carrying things. Dr. George M. Dawson, who penetrated the area in 1876, encountered about 60 Indians on these trails. "Every man, woman and child, and even some dogs, with packs of appropriate size. All appeared to be in good spirits." On his recent visits Mr. Swannell saw the same sight. "They would be Indians from about

---

* Ulkatcho is on today's maps. Mr. Swannell, who visited it in 1926, found the same tribe still there, but today the "civilized Indians" live in a score of tumbledown cabins.

2,500 square miles of mountain wilderness. One wonders how many years, perhaps hundreds, this annual trek has been made."

The Ulkatchos informed Mackenzie that their ultimate market was "white people who arrive in large canoes," but these they had never seen. They had only been informed about them by the Bella Coolas, who in turn had heard about the white men from the Coast Indians on the islands and fjords.

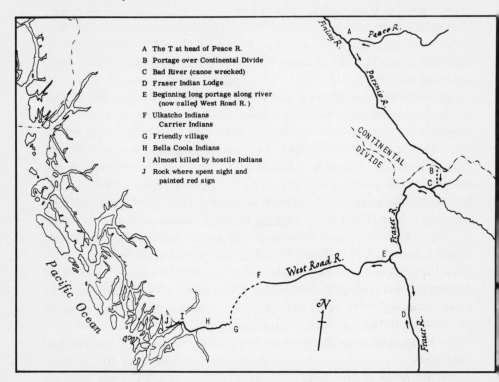

A The T at head of Peace R.
B Portage over Continental Divide
C Bad River (canoe wrecked)
D Fraser Indian Lodge
E Beginning long portage along river
   (now called West Road R.)
F Ulkatcho Indians
   Carrier Indians
G Friendly village
H Bella Coola Indians
I Almost killed by hostile Indians
J Rock where spent night and
   painted red sign

Confronted by the "stupendous mountain," Alexander Mackenzie's 1793 brigade was nearly across the great blank on the map that was the Mountain and Coast Forest merger. A savage climax awaited them.

While laboriously plodding along, wading through streams, climbing over fallen trees, like a file of tiny ants in the immensity, they fell in with Carrier Indians going their way, as their friends on the Fraser had predicted. The Ulkatcho Carriers also had never seen white men; they were all agog, friendly and offered to show Mackenzie a short cut down into the valley to a river leading to the sea. It must have seemed to the footsore, pack-laden brigade, that at last their troubles were over. During the next day Mackenzie saw the mountains parting, and valleys opening toward the west.

Guided on the short cut by the Ulkatchos, they crossed a 6-thousand-foot summit, the highest point of their entire trip, and then zigzagged for 35 miles down precipitous mountain sides where there was no trail—to drop out of the sky into a community of Bella Coola Indians. This is labeled "friendly village" on Mackenzie's chart.

This was the goal of the Ulkatchos, who proceeded to trade their furs from interior mountain valleys for the ivory teeth of seals and sea lions, perhaps the rare treasure of a Pacific walrus tusk, mother of pearl, woven cedar bark, goats'-wool blankets and, above all, "stinking grease" from decaying candle-fish.*

After several days of excitement, gestures and ceremony, the brigade climbed into Bella Coola canoes (this time, and so far as I know the only time on record, *les voyageurs des bois* were passengers) and started on a 60-mile trip down a fine river to its mouth at the head of a Pacific Ocean fjord. But not before the Bella Coolas gave an astounding exhibition of paddling. They could take a canoe leaping among rocks and waterfalls at great speed, and jump it over a 4-foot weir without shipping a drop. Even *les voyageurs* admired the feat.

They reached tidewater at what is now called North Bentinck Arm of Burke Channel, but it didn't look like the seacoast. This long narrow fjord that extends 70 miles inland from the open sea looks like a wide deep river, between 700-foot cliffs, with cedar, spruce, fir and white birch crowding every patch of soil. So far from the open ocean, and fed by fresh mountain streams, the surface water at this spot would taste fresh. Mackenzie and his men were not convinced that they had reached their goal.

At the head of the fjord, the Bella Coolas reached their national boundary but they lent Mackenzie one of their large canoes, pointed northwest as the direction of the ocean, and after warnings about murderous people, disappeared to some mysterious place to trade with Coast Indians. The brigade paddled about 50 miles farther down the fjord. As they went, they caught the fragrance of seaweed in the wind and the water grew saltier. Three canoes with strange Indians put out from the shore,

* An edible, oily smeltlike fish of northern Pacific water which, after decaying and drying, burns like a candle.

looked them over and disappeared. Mackenzie tells in his own telegraphic style what happened next:

> We went on with great velocity. Surrounding hills in fog. Strong west wind in face. Bay about a mile or more in breadth. Tide was out. Lots of seaweed . . . walked along the land. Saw great numbers of sea otter. Tried to shoot, but they plunged into the water too fast. Saw porpoises, white-headed eagle, gulls, ducks. Tide 15 feet. Shifted baggage several times. Troublesome fellow forced himself into canoe. Wanted to see instruments. Wanted hat, handkerchief, etc. Ten canoes with four men each . . . stole everything.

One Indian that Mackenzie was trying to question led him into "bad road encumbered with underwood. Surprised to see two men running toward me with daggers in their hands and fury in their aspect. Brandished gun. Made them let go their daggers, which were fastened to a string around their wrists."

The Indians came, one after the other. One grabbed Mackenzie from behind, but his friends came out of the woods just in time. "These people might have successfully dispatched every one of us. If they had killed me, this consequence would certainly have followed, and not one of us would have returned home to tell the horrid fate of his companions."

When they were unloading dunnage and preparing to camp for the night, a young Indian (one of the two he had brought along from Athabaska?) entreated him to leave before arrows and spears began to fly. "In relating our danger, his agitation was so violent that he foamed at the mouth. My people were panic-struck. It was necessary to disguise my apprehension."

Mackenzie was inexorable. This was the spot which he had spent two years preparing to reach. For this place he had brought all the way from London instruments to determine the latitude and longitude. He was determined to stay until the clouds broke enough to give him a shot at the sun.

They took possession of a rock with "not space enough for more than a third our number," made a fire and set up a roster for two men to be awake and on guard continuously while others slept. The next day was cloudy. They held on for another night. During that tense overcast day Mackenzie took the package of vermilion out of his pack, mixed it with animal grease melted in a fire and painted in large letters on the rock:

ALEXANDER MACKENZIE FROM CANADA BY
LAND THE 22ND OF JULY ONE THOU-
SAND SEVEN HUNDRED AND NINETY-THREE.

"From Canada," that was a far-away country. "By land?"—most of
the way by canoe!

Early the second morning, the sun flashed briefly through a rift in the
clouds. Mackenzie got his bearings. They scrambled into the canoe and
with a few quick strokes of six paddles they disappeared into the mist
that hung over the fjord.

On August 24, Mackenzie's brigade, all ten of them, returned to the
little winter fort near the mouth of the Peace River, from which they had
departed. In 74 days they had traveled 1,200 miles, 940 miles by canoe,
260 miles back-packing overland.

After that, the Mountain Forest and the Coast Forest obliterated Alexander Mackenzie's route between the North Woods and the Pacific Coast.
It was as though he had never been there.

People who have gone to look in recent years have found the land-
marks which he clearly described in his dry factual account, showing the
route of his fantastic canoe trip to the coast and back. But nobody has
followed that exact route by any method of travel since. Our maps show
that Mackenzie tackled the most impregnable mountain fastness, where
some of the highest Rocky Mountains ranges converge with the loftiest
Coast Ranges. The glacier-covered mountain ranges, with giant pines on
steep mountainsides, and roaring of cataracts in dark deep canyons are
still as Mackenzie beheld them.

chapter sixteen

Mountain and Coastal Forests

THE Mountain Forest and the Coast Forest merge in British Columbia to form an immense, almost incalculable conifer empire. An airplane following the Pacific coastline from the Katmai National Monument in Alaska to the Olympic National Park in Washington State would travel about 2 thousand miles. But the actual length of the shores of this wilderness is virtually immeasurable. On countless islands, the dark conifers crowd the shorelines of fjords, some of which run inland for more than a hundred miles. The fragmented, seemingly endless coastline is a remarkable feature of this wilderness. Here flourish unique species of conifers—western red cedar that raises a 200-foot shaft of decay- and insect-proof wood, out of rain soaked ground; Alaska cedar, with foliage like lacy fans which droop and revolve inward toward the trunk, making the tree look like a collapsed tent dangling on a tall rigid pole, and Sitka spruce, perhaps the most storm-resistant tree on earth, with needles seemingly as hard and sharp as steel. The crown of Sitka spruce is flat and formed to spill the wind; its branches, which all point inland with the airflow, are rigid streamers twanging in the sea blast.

It is appropriate that such rugged forest, with salmon-laden streams, should be the home of the world's largest carnivore, the Alaska brown bear, which weighs three quarters of a ton and stands 12 feet when it rears up on its hind legs.* With all its bulk and apparent clumsiness, this bear can gallop much faster than a fleeing man, proceeding on a tangent so as to watch behind him as well as ahead. Moreover, the giant bear has been seen to scale an almost vertical 30-foot cliff to reach a moose carcass, using its long curved foreclaws like iron hooks in rock crevices. The Katmai National Monument, about 3,800 square miles, is the last refuge on earth of this magnificent wilderness monster.

The width of the northwest wilderness also defies reckoning. A succession of ridges of the highest mountain ranges of the continent run side by side to form this great wilderness. It narrows where the mountain chains converge at the elbow around the Gulf of Alaska, and widens where they separate in British Columbia, forming high valleys and broad basins between snow-covered ranges. Mackenzie tackled the middle of this forest belt, where it is about 400 miles wide in a straight line on our maps, and where it has a third dimension. A brigade traveling across the mountain ranges can only move forward by climbing and descending great vertical distances.

This rugged feature of the region makes it dramatically different from the other major forest areas of North America. We have seen how French and English pioneer fur traders could move in any direction by canoes and portages through the vast North Woods. The luxurious deciduous wilderness of the East has its Allegheny ranges, running from Maine to Georgia. They were a formidable barrier only to the earliest English colonists. Here are no mountains snow-capped the year round, and the Mohawk River valley offers an easy waterway in a pleasant valley through the Alleghenies. In 1753, a young man, 21 years old, named George Washington, went through the heart of the Alleghenies to the headwaters of the Ohio River, and a few years later Washington led an army detachment across and established a post they called "Pittsbourgh." By the time Mackenzie was accepting the awesome challenge of the Rocky Mountains, some 300 thousand settlers had reached Kentucky and beyond, mainly through the Cumberland Gap.

The formidable vertical reaches of the Mountain Forest do not extend south of the United States border. Here the Rocky Mountains and the Coast Ranges diverge and, although an even higher range, the

---

* This behavior of the monster inspired Kipling's bloodcurdling poem about "the bear that walks like a man."

Sierras, is interposed between them, the nineteenth century pioneers found many passes and established well-worn trails around and through those mountains and across the deserts and basins between them.

The main-line route was the famous 2 thousand-mile Oregon Trail through the mountains of Wyoming and Idaho and on into Oregon. The Mormons pushed their flimsy handcarts over this trail, branching off into Utah. The covered wagons were rolling into California long before the gold rush along the California Trail that branched off at South Pass, Wyoming, to cross Nevada. The Butterfield Overland Stage Route ran from St. Louis to San Francisco by skirting the south end of the High Sierras. The Pony Express riders whipped and hollered their mustangs from St. Joseph, Missouri, to Sacramento, California, on well-worn trails through northern mountain passes. On the other hand, no stage coach has ever lurched and no man has ever ridden a horse (and never will) across the ranges of the merged Mountain and Coast Forests of British Columbia.

It has been tried. In 1932 a wealthy French sportsman and daredevil named Charles Bedaux turned up at a trading post community on the navigable lower Peace River east of the Rocky Mountains. His hunting expedition had produced marvelous trophies and he was in a conquering, jovial mood when he heard a bunch of traders and trappers voice the old yearning for an outlet through the mountains to the Pacific. M. Bedaux, his confidence high because he had been the first man to cross the Sahara Desert by motor, wagered that he could get a party from that trading post through the mountains to the Pacific. The wager was accepted by the local tough *hombres,* so two years later Bedaux was back, prepared to duplicate Mackenzie's feat after 141 years. The difference was that Mackenzie had set out in a canoe because he didn't know the mountains were there, while Bedaux, who could see the mountains, set out with axes, shovels, manpower and automobile horsepower.

They were 47 strong in the party, some mounted and leading a string of packhorses, others riding in six Citroën cars in low gear, moving slowly toward the mountains along the banks of the Peace River. Their equipment included cameras, folding bathtubs, Arab tents and a case of champagne to celebrate their arrival on the Pacific Coast. They toiled for about fifty miles until the cars were hopelessly balked at the base of the first line of foothills. The men had plenty of well-trained horses for such a contingency. They mounted and wound in single file up the steep slopes.

Three days later, before they had reached the first of the main ranges of the Rockies, the horses' feet were bruised and heavy loads had to be rearranged. Then all of the packhorses developed foot-rot and the expedition foundered. The pitiable animals and the equipment were abandoned. The men straggled down to the Peace River, where they built rafts and rode the currents back to the trading post from which they had started. Bedaux brought back a few geologic records and enhanced his reputation as a melodramatic hotspur, for which he paid half a million dollars of equipment and wages.

The Mountain Forest is a thrilling exhibit of the work of the three wilderness architects—ice, water and fire. Earthquakes repeatedly rumble through this area, making the great mountains tremble. Volcanoes explode through the earth's crust, and pour out fiery lava. Orogeny (mountain building by subterranean forces) is still pushing up those towering ranges, whose rocks in a late epoch were sediments at the bottom of the sea. Glaciers from the recent Ice Age remain in high ravines, and, fed by blizzards on the peaks above, their fingers creep down valleys to vanish at the edge of Arctic tundra on high plateaus surrounded by dark conifer forests.

The work of the architect water begins each year when the spring thaw of glaciers and winter snows releases roaring cataracts and fast floods that cut ravines and widen valleys in all directions. In summer when the swollen waters have subsided and valleys on the leeward side of the ranges may be desert dry, the sculpturing of rocks is continued at a furious pace by cloudbursts that are generated around lofty peaks.

In our human perspective, the work of architect fire is not an everyday event. An earthquake or eruption that alters valleys and mountains seems to us an unusual accident instead of a repeat performance. Such events have been occurring regularly throughout the earth's history. When the Alaska end of the northwestern wilderness shrugged its shoulders in March 1964, the earthquake damaged human assets to the extent of over 300 million dollars, but alterations to the great Coast Forest were not unusual.

Katmai National Monument, today by far the largest unit in the United States National Park System (mentioned above as the refuge of the Alaska brown bear that walks like a man) was created almost instantaneously by a big bang in June 1912, after a prelude of violent earthquakes that convulsed the ground and swayed the forests along the coast for two days. Then a relatively insignificant mountain, now called Novarupta, gave an enormous sneeze, hurling out glowing avalanches of sand and hot gases. The fumes stung the lungs of people on Vancouver Island a thousand miles away. Two and a half cubic miles of volcanic material were ejected, and their avalanches and fountains of fiery dust buried the floor of the valley, three to six miles wide and fifteen miles long, under *seven hundred feet* of steaming pumice and lava. To this day, steam is pouring out of fumeroles across forty square miles of an area called The Valley of Ten Thousand Smokes, an interesting new Alaskan terminus for the Coast Forest.

This natural act of architect fire had a staggering finale. Six miles east of the original crater rose white-topped 7-thousand-foot Mount Katmai, landmark of the Klondike gold-rushers, whose chief trail had passed that way in '99. The mountains in that part of the Coast Forest were holding down tremendous pressures of gases in a connected system of caverns filled with seething lava. A few days after the awful pressure was relieved by the explosion of Novarupta, the upper third of Mount Katmai, with its snow fields, glaciers and rocky cliffs, vanished in a caldera of boiling lava three miles wide and six miles long.

Although this event astounds us, it is standard procedure in wilderness building. Visitors at the Volcano House in the Hawaiian national park stare into Halemaumau (Polynesian for Great Fire Pit) where 750 feet below the rim a floor 2½ miles long and 2 miles wide is rumbling, steaming and occasionally shooting up fountains of fiery sparks. Here the towering dome of still fiery Kilauea collapsed before Hawaii was discovered.

In the Coast Forest of southwestern Oregon, Crater Lake is a silent, utterly beautiful turquoise jewel, mounted a mile high on the stump of Mt. Mazama, which was once the highest mountain in the area. It had been 12 thousand feet high. Around four thousand years ago the spectacular heights of snow fields, sparkling white in the sunlight, and the black canyons in ancient rocks, were suddenly turned bright red by fountains of glowing pumice. A few weeks later, terror-stricken people in an Indian village 25 miles away saw the upper half of Mazama collapse and drop into a profound cavern, where pressures great enough to hold up the mountain had been relieved by the eruptions.

Due to its verticality, the Mountain Forest in British Columbia has continued in an almost primeval state, less damaged by man than any other big forest region of the continent. Here are still sounds of falling water that human ears have not heard, streams where men have not fished, colonies of animals and birds which men have not seen. Other great forests have an almost uniform texture and comparable wild life. This one is variable, unpredictable, with dim mysterious solitudes of ice and snow above, and a melange of canyons, alpine meadows, grassy prairies and vast dark forest below. Many sorts of natural phenomena are thrown together, literally on top of each other.

Yet the Mountain Forest is not confused. Everything is in the right place. In a natural wilderness, evolution appears to have reached a stage of stability. It has long been, and always will be as it is—so it seems. Foresters speak of a climax forest.

One of the greatest mountain peaks in British Columbia went un-named until recently. Let mountain climber Prescott Fay, of Boston, tell his story: *

"A high pass of 7,500 feet led north. The upland meadows, sparsely covered with stunted balsam and spruces, were bright with flowers. We halted to watch a mountain goat as he laboriously worked his way along the other side of the pass. The snow through which he was plowing was deep and the going heavy, so that he became winded and his tongue hung out of his wide-open mouth like a dog's. After frequent stops to get his wind, he finally reached the rock wall. The sheer walls gave him considerable difficulty, and once as he reached far up with his front feet in order to pull himself to the ledge above, he slipped and fell over back-wards. We thought he would be dashed to pieces on the rocks, but in falling he turned in the air like a cat and dropped nimbly on all four feet on a narrow jutting rock. We could hardly believe our eyes.

"We climbed to a ridge and had our best view of the big mountain, six miles away. Its base is sheer rocky cliffs, above which a large glacier en-circles the final peak which rises about 3 thousand feet higher. There was one hanging glacier. Its falling ice sounded like thunder on the rocks below.

"Next morning, a fine, clear August day, we climbed 2 thousand feet above the camp where we saw a brilliant region of snow and ice and another big white summit of a giant mountain. Extremely dangerous to

* *Beaver Magazine*, publication of The Hudson's Bay Company, Autumn 1957.

climb because of steep and hazardous ice slopes and an ice cornice on top. . . . We regretted not staying longer to explore the big new mountain, but time was valuable and utterly trail-less country lay ahead, through which we journeyed almost continuously, climbing to an eminence to lay our course ahead. We were four months reaching the Peace River, and for many weeks the mountain served as a landmark and aided us in our map-making.

"In the absence of any name for this big new mountain, we called it Mount Sir Alexander, after intrepid Alexander Mackenzie, who had passed only a few miles to the west of it. This name was later approved by the Geographic Board of Canada."

Elevations in the valley, and lower slopes of the mountains are covered by dense forests of Englemann spruce, lodgepole pine, Alpine fir, western paper birch—the haunts of wolverine, lynx, black bear and cougar. However, these fascinating forests are only one feature of the mountain-to-mountain carpeting of this valley empire. Thousand-acre alpine meadows form sunny patches of colorful Indian paintbrush, rosy sedum, mountain craneberry, bearberry, andromeda, cassiope; teem with conies, ptarmigan, snowshoe rabbits; are crisscrossed by the trails of coyote, moose and wolf.

On the Fraser River, a rare intruder might hear the song of Townsend's solitaire coming from a willow thicket. Nature detached this shy thrush from its relatives in tropical America and isolated it in the remote northern valleys of the Mountain Forest, where it sings for very few human ears, "a flute-like melody, the loveliest bird song."

The landscape is brimming with free-living populations of animals and birds all in their places in the chain of life, which begins underground, mounts to the forest floor, to the tall tree canopies, to the eagles in the air. For those of us who feel the call of the wild, who are invigorated by snowy mountains, delighted by spires of tall trees standing geometrically perpendicular on steep slopes, who enjoy the majesty of a moose, the suppleness of a deer, the clowning of a wolverine, the craftsmanship of a beaver—this sanctuary exists.

To some men the area was neither sanctuary nor wilderness, as we think of it. They were, of course, the Indians who built their homes here —the Ulkatchos, the Carrier Indians, and others.

Mackenzie wrote 172 years ago, "Every man, woman and child carried a burden, consisting of beaver coating, skins of otter, marten, bear, lynx and dressed moose hides. The last they procured from the Rocky Mountain Indians (the tribe in the Fraser Valley). They say that the people on the coast prefer the moose skins to any other article. The people on the coast barter in their turn with white people who, as they have been informed, arrive in large canoes."

These few words give us the sole eye-witness account of an astonishing vigorous culture that flourished in the solitude of this merger of the Coast and Mountain Forests before it was seen by white men. Here are nations in the embryonic tribal stage, as they were in Britain when the Angles and Saxons arrived. The Indian tribes were expanded families. They had a common language root, but different ways of life produced linguistic differences. The interior valley people were influenced by moose, beaver, grouse and berries; the coast people, by deep-sea fish, shell fish, sea otter, seal and the dark, tall timber which made them master craftsmen and wood-carvers; the Carrier tribes in the mountains were hunters, trout fishers and long-distance travelers across a network of moccasin and canoe trails.

Westerners came upon this ancient culture intact in the seclusion of the great northwestern conifer forests, where it survived for thousands of years after the prehistoric cultures of the Old World had vanished. Indeed, tribes in British Columbia still reflect, in the 1960's, some of their ancient ways, preserved among the snow-capped mountains, tortuous ravines and cold tides.

The descendants of the Indians whom Mackenzie saw are still hunting, fishing and trading, although now "civilized." They live in tumbledown cabins instead of durable lodges built of heavy, mortised timbers, magnificently painted and carved with the emblems of their ancestors. When Mackenzie passed that way they were in natural balance with the forest, living freely in the midst of abundance. Today, the country is destitute of game and the forest much burnt over, and horse trails, in wretched shape, are hopelessly impassable in places. "The old moccasin trails of Mackenzie's day were in much better condition," say the reports of government surveyors.

The cultures of the Indians of the Coast Forest were no less creative and elaborate than the Mayan, Aztec and Inca cultures, but were expressed in different terms. Whereas the latter were based on grain crops and the people built with stone, the cultures of the northwestern Indians were based on fish and furs, and they built with beautiful timber. The Indians in the North Woods and in the eastern deciduous forest had a diffuse culture, with many skills, among which the art of the birchbark canoe is outstanding, but they were nomadic, without clearly defined national territories. They created no permanent habitation. Structures such as the earthen mounds, many similar to the Great Serpent Mound in southern Ohio, were comparatively crude.

Each nation in the northwestern Coast Forest was stabilized in its own territory. Coast Indians on certain islands held a franchise for fishing in particular waters, a Carrier tribe had its own river or mountain pass, a Rocky Mountain tribe hunted and fished in its homeland valley. Their lodges and totem poles were permanent, enlarged and carved from generation to generation. Their respect for national boundaries is seen in the way international trade was conducted by trading from one tribe to the next.

A piece of stirring news has recently come from the Peace River Block which shows how that area has been comparatively isolated from human intrusion for the 172 years since Mackenzie visited it.

The area has had public attention in recent years directed to the heroic efforts to save the whooping crane from extinction. That great primeval bird has come to be regarded as a rare American heirloom, a symbol of a legacy that is slipping through our fingers. Here is a tangible, beautiful, living thing that people can see—a snow white bird with a 7½ foot wingspread, slowly stroking the air in a blue sky. Only one small flock survives, its pitifully few members can be counted at their winter home on the Texas Gulf Coast where they still arrive on schedule each fall. A baby whooping crane is reported by the newspapers from coast to coast. People have waited for the annual whooping crane count with tingling spines as though it were some kind of a national lottery—a low of 23 in 1941, up to 36 in 1960, in 1965—42, the highest count since the annual tally began 26 years ago. Yet what a slight margin in a contest with extinction!

Where the flock went after disappearing in the sky over the North Woods was a mystery until the National Audubon Society retained Robert Tate Allen to find out. He sought the breeding ground for four years, enlisting the help of thousands of observers. Finally, in 1954, a man in a helicopter flying low over the sanctum sanctorum of the Peace River Block caught the glint of bright white spots moving in a large clump of bulrushes. They turned out to be some adult whooping cranes with one young bird. In this way the breeding spot of the only whooping cranes on earth was discovered among many square miles of pothole muskeg, perhaps the largest tract of untouched wild-life country on the continent today. In 1955, Allen and a Canadian official went in by helicopter and camped for ten days in a grove of black spruce and larch on a tiny island, watching the whooping cranes in (to use Allen's words) "a magnificent wilderness where no man, white or Indian, had ever set foot before us!"

The huge, famous herds of American bison were a thousand miles south of the Peace River on the western prairies of the United States and those prairies had not even been crossed by white men at the time of Mackenzie's expedition. However, the bison were well known along the Mississippi as the mainstay of Indian tribes and the shaggy old animal had long been called buffalo by the Spaniards. The first mention of a large herd which made the ground rumble and shake came from the Lewis and Clark expedition in 1805. The tragic story of the bison is familiar—the national disgrace when 60 million animals on the western plains at the time the white man arrived were wiped out in the wanton slaughter of the 1870's. In that decade fortunes were made from the sale of buffalo tongues at 25 cents each, leaving for each tongue half a ton of fine meat to rot on the plain. The last of the wild plains bison—two bulls, a lonely cow and her calf—were killed in Colorado in 1897. Today they are on exhibit in the Denver Museum of Natural History. By 1900 only a few hundred dreary bison survived in corrals—with one surprising exception.

In 1893 a Manitoba man was in Edmonton, Alberta, on business when he saw in a fur warehouse twenty fine buffalo heads and robes. Back home in Winnipeg he mentioned this to a friend connected with a newspaper. This stirred up a treasure hunt which led to an Indian tribe in northern Alberta who said that they had killed more than two hundred bison the summer before in an area south of Great Slave Lake.

Thus the lost herd of bison was discovered in the wilderness of the Peace River Block. They are a strain known as wood bison, a little larger, a little taller than those of the plains. The herd was increasing so rapidly that Canadian officials issued permits for hunting buffalo in 1959 —the only wild buffalo hunt of this century. A reliable report puts the number of bison in the Peace River Block herd today as more than 40,000 head.

Perhaps millennia earlier, in the wake of the melting glaciers of the Ice Age, they had pushed their migrations much farther north to a lost home in an unknown land. Or perhaps their ancestors escaped from the holocaust of the 1870's by lumbering into the wild-life vault on the Peace River Block, where they survived with the whooping cranes. We shall never know.

chapter seventeen

Our Vanishing Wildness

CURRENT events are snatching these pages from my hands as I write them. The Peace River Block, so hauntingly detached from or tumultuous world, was featured in a full page story in *The National Observer* (December 7, 1964) headlined: "New Rails Cut Path To Canada's Riches." As the rail builders roll north on the Great Slave Lake Railway they are "opening up millions of acres." Here is, indeed, stirring news: "the surveying crew, riding ahead on a snowmobile, slogging alongside a bulldozer, Mr. Cox overhead in a bubble-nosed helicopter scouting out the best path through the forest. The 'dozer man would take a bearing on the hovering copter, then crash forward through the trees."

I wonder what the lone family of whooping cranes and the last herd of free bison—two peerless emblems of America—will do when they hear the shouting, crashing cavalcade approaching? If they were paintings on the wall of a cave or fossils, instead of flesh and blood, their story would have a different thrill, and money would pour forth to enshrine them.

In the chapter about fabulous conifers, we stood on a green carpet in a twilight hush, and looked up and up at astounding columns ten times higher than the pillars of the Parthenon. Surely the patch of ground where those redwoods grow is sacred soil. Few people realize that some

200 thousand acres of virgin-growth redwoods (including the tallest living thing on earth, a tree as high as a 35-story building!) are owned by lumber companies. There were 1.8 million acres before lumbering commenced. At the rate they are now being felled and sawed up, they will all be gone in 20 years, leaving a remnant of redwoods protected in 50 thousand acres of State Parks.

The California State Highway Commission has announced plans to drive a wide, multilane freeway through the 7-thousand-acre National Tribute Grove. This stateliest, loveliest and hushed area in the Jedediah Smith Redwoods State Park was purchased through the heroic efforts of the Save-the-Redwoods League by gifts of money and land from more than 4 thousand people all over the United States—to be set aside as a living memorial to relatives and friends who served their country in the war. A similar plan threatens dedicated groves in nearby Prairie Creek Redwoods State Park, and Humboldt Redwoods State Park, once considered the finest park, has already succumbed to a freeway.

Who can say, "it is in the public interest" to let poisonous gases from exhausts fill the fragrant misty twilight under the redwood canopy and leave serene giants standing on the remains of their severed sacred ground, quivering in the uproar of tremendous trailer-trucks. If their cathedral had been wrought in stone by man, instead of in living cells by sunlight . . . why doesn't a redwood cathedral inspire equal reverence?

It surely does in many people, but not among the modern cultists of concrete. California's governor terms the destruction of redwoods "sacrilegious," but the Highway Commission is practically autonomous. There seems no hope. Funds are in hand to buy the right-of-way. Eighty acres of the finest primeval forest will be lost in a one mile stretch. Another mile of pledged private lands will also be lost.

What about the smashing bulldozer assaults on countless other forest places? For example, do we have to spread concrete on every mile of the crest ridge of the Great Smokies, even where the Southern Appalachian Trail for hikers now runs? Apparently we do—to connect the Blue Ridge Parkway with an interstate highway at a cost of $73 million to down the trees on this beautiful forested ridge and put concrete where they stand. That is the appropriation requested of Congress, but it will take more millions for access and exit concrete, picnic, service and maintenance areas.

The North Woods, that marvelous transcontinental forest which still holds much fascinating American wildness, sent a lobe down the Yukon River to spread over interior Alaska south of Mt. McKinley. As recently as 1956 some 36 million acres of these interior Alaskan virgin forests were called inaccessible. Today a portentous proposal comes from the Corps of Army Engineers in Washington, not to make the vast, virgin forest accessible, but to blot it out. It is proposed to achieve this by building the Rampart Dam on the Yukon for a billion dollars. The figure does not include the cost of building 1,500 miles of power transmission lines through the Rocky Mountain forests to Washington and Oregon.

Rampart Dam, 530 feet high, 4,700 feet across, 100 miles northwest of Fairbanks, will obliterate at one fell swoop the homes of mink, muskrat, moose, beaver, bear, fox and other fur-bearing animals totaling 3,500 *million,* according to an estimate of the Fish and Wildlife Service. In addition it will deal a fatal blow to uncountable millions of Yukon salmon, and to the breeding grounds of myriads of ducks and geese, not to mention the disaster visited upon 2,000 native Alaskans whose lives revolve around these resources. The Senator from Alaska leads the cheering, but the dazzling development does not overawe an editorial writer of the *New York Times* (March 8, 1965) who asks whether Rampart Dam will turn out to be "the world's biggest sinkhole for public funds?"

A brightly colored circular promoting Rampart sings the refrain about "recreational potential of the 280-mile long lake, unlimited fresh water boating and sailing, hunting lodges, camps." The *Alaska Review* answers —"Recreation? Watersports? Does one hear about aquatic recreation on Great Slave Lake which lies at a comparable location geographically and climatically? Not with ice that lasts until mid-summer, and winds that whip up waves as large as on the Great Lakes. Scenic beaches? Not with muddy, stump-strewn fluctuating shore lines caused by power drawdowns."

A few years ago Columbia Falls in northwest Montana, a community of about 1,200 people, was in trouble when its lumber industry died for lack of trees. Then came a windfall in the form of Hungry Horse Dam. One could be sincerely glad that the economy of the town was saved with the opportunity to create a new national asset. But when the millions were spent and the dam was built there came another wail to save Columbia Falls. The Corps of Army Engineers responded with some real big thinking for Glacier National Park a few miles north of Columbia Falls. That magnificent park had been established in 1940 to protect for all time for all Americans over a million acres of spectacular mountain peaks and primeval forests. But Glacier National Park offered the ideal location for the great Glacier View Dam.

What started as a local aid project has ballooned into a multi-million dollar plan in the heart of a splendid National Park that would blot out 80 thousand acres of untouched forest, the habitats of black bear and grizzly, Rocky Mountain bighorn, coyote, elk, moose and mountain lion. The area proposed for drowning is the foreground setting for the peaks of famous Glacier View. The abuse of this marvelous National Park is compounded by a plan for another great dam in the same region, Spruce Park Dam, that will alter the natural flow of the Middle Fork of the Flathead River which forms for many miles the south border of Glacier National Park.

Here are three myths about conservation:

- People who feel concern about our vanishing wildness can relax and leave it to the authorities because of the Wilderness Act of 1964.
- Historic loved and noble forests and spectacular scenery are safe in National Parks.
- The best way to conserve water for survival in the face of an exploding population is to build more tremendous dams at any cost.

To these three myths it is appropriate to add a matter of sheer casuistry—that "managed forests" and "multiple use forests" somehow justify the plundering of surviving remnants of the ancient irreplaceable forests of trees taller than 20-story buildings.

To insure future supplies of lumber, wood pulp and cellulose by "forest management" is in the best tradition of American industry. People are told that the lumber and paper companies are growing more wood than they are cutting. This happy fact relates to the growth of the *annual increments*. Seedlings, saplings, one-year of added wood rings will never restore true wildness despite appealing color advertisements of deer, beaver and bobwhites in managed forests. If forest managers wait 500 years (which they will not) will the managed forest then be the home of deer, bear, cougar, beaver and wolverine? Will there be wild flowers and berry-laden bushes? Will there be ferns, mosses and lichens, lakes, streams with trout, ponds teeming with ducks? Will bighorn be surveying dark spires from a rocky shoulder, and will the bugling of the wapiti be heard in the managed forest? American wilderness is bequeathed to us only once; destroyed, it is unrestorable.

When the commotion about cutting the last stands of ancient redwoods was at its height, a feature story by a spokesman for the lumber and paper industries appeared in *American Forests,* September, 1964, under this heading: "World's Tallest Tree Farm—Follow-up for the Future." Enthusiastically, in bold face type, the story said, "Redwoods genetics research, plus the establishment of more second growth redwood groves as parks for the future could go far toward insuring redwoods for both use and enjoyment forever." So much for sheer casuistry.

It may be argued that the great timber trees—Douglas fir, redwood, western red cedar, western white pine, the tall firs in the mountain and coast forests, and ponderosa pine are part of the wealth of the people and that we must use them to make ourselves richer and to provide more comfortable homes. Perhaps—when the ancient forests with their birds, animals and flowers seemed limitless. But should the bulldozers drive ahead, and heavy-duty trailers rumble out of the pitiful remnants of the stately virgin forest, bearing logs 10 to 15 feet in diameter, this magnificent wealth of our land will be completely consumed—in just a few more years.

The lumber and paper industries themselves are supplying some practical alternatives. They are awakening farmers to the opportunity for profit by growing tree farms. They are arousing the public to the waste and loss of forest fires. They are encouraging community forests, school forests and Christmas tree plantations, and they are increasingly growing trees as crops. These are good answers as far as they go—but the bulldozers still smash ahead, the majestic irreplaceable trees still crash and the birds and animals, the inspiration of our traditions, the symbols of our forest inheritance, huddle in the ever-decreasing areas where a few still survive.

The great contribution of the Wilderness Act is that it made our vanishing wildness a subject of lively debate in Congress and gave it wide publicity. If it only gives pause to the cult of concrete before irrevocable damage is done in some places, if it is only a check on dam builders' schemes before they commit inutterable folly in the name of the people, the Wilderness Act should be acclaimed. The wonder is that it could be passed at all in the hue and cry for "development," in which "recreational value" is tainted by the old impulse for "the conquest of nature."

The Wilderness Act declares it to be the policy of the Congress of the United States "to secure for the American people of present and future generations the benefits of an enduring resource of wilderness." It strengthens the hand of the National Park Service in resisting the pressures for roads, resort structures, reservoirs and many other projects that continually bite into the National Park System.

The myth is that the Wilderness Act of 1964 has made secure America's heritage of wilderness, has put a stop to mining, oil drilling and commercial exploitation, has removed from the pressure of politics and local interests future attempts at exploitation, that by this Act wild remnants will remain wild, and the great dams cannot be built and reservoirs created which will deface or drown any areas included in the National Wilderness Preservation System. But this is not so. Congress, with due respect for the pressure of politics and lobbies, will decide how the Wilderness Act works. This means that despite the passage of the Wilderness Act a powerful, articulate public opinion in behalf of our American forests and wilderness is needed *now more than ever*.

The Wilderness Act does not close down any mining or oil well activities, nor does it prohibit in that connection the cutting and removal of mature timber, which means bulldozing for access roads and transportation lines. Aircraft and motor boats may continue to use waterways where they are already doing so. Mining, prospecting, oil and gas development will be permitted for the next 19 years in the National Forest areas of the Wilderness Preservation System. This Act does not cancel any grazing permit or hunting license in accord with state game laws. State and private water rights are not affected. The President can allow, on his own, the construction of reservoirs, transmission lines and other facilities within wilderness areas if he deems these to be in the public interest. The Act permits "commercial services which are necessary for realizing the recreational and other wilderness purposes."

In all official discussion of the National Wilderness Preservation System "conservation" is linked with other words—recreational, scenic, scientific, educational, historical use. Who decides what these mean in terms of highways, parking areas, and other structures? A feature writer in *American Forests* asserts that "logging is an important tool in the development of recreational uses of the national forests." Yet the Act eloquently defines "wilderness" as an area "where the earth and its community of life are untrammeled by man."

The Wilderness Act vaunts more than it delivers, but many people are responding to the values inherent in its title and idea. May the intensity of their interest exert pressure for saving the remnants of our wildness that remain. Enough people must crave some of these assets for themselves and their children. The wildness of our continent is a quality of life for all Americans whether or not they personally see it. The mere idea of hushed places among big trunks, of the nose of a moose cutting a V across a glassy lake, of pure silvery water running in a brook, of salmon leaping up a waterfall, of bloodroot and partridge berry on a leaf carpet and skunk cabbage uncoiling its mottled shells among pussy willows; beaver, fox, and deer with big round eyes—the knowledge that such things exist, that there is a North Woods, an unspoiled area in the deciduous forest, a deep silent valley in the Rocky Mountains, enhances the value of every county park, hedgerow and woodlot.

We must awaken to this now, not ten years from now. These values are irrevocable. You cannot whistle back the tall columns, the deep humus, the millions of animals and birds in Alaska's great interior forest, the silvery brook, the pure well water. In that imaginary time when dams and developments have been completed, no bureau like the Outdoor Recreation Resources Review Commission can restore any vanished wildness, not with ten times the billions given to the cult of concrete and the dam-builders.

The third great myth pertains to water conservation. Water for survival has suddenly become an overwhelming national emergency. The water crisis arose imperceptibly in this locality, in that locality, where forests were cut in this watershed, in that watershed, where brush land, swamp, and pasture were bulldozed for real estate development or thruways.

In 1962 at the request of the President, the Committee of Natural Resources, consisting of twelve men of the highest authority, published a remarkable report based on a year's research and consultation with 172 scientists, engineers and industrial leaders. This astute and authoritative report said:

> Man is altering the balance of a relatively stable system by his alteration of the energy and water balance at the earth's surface by deforestation . . . reduction of evapo-transpiration, irrigation, drainage of large swamplands, the building of highways, his clearing forests and alterations of the plants' surface cover . . . by his land filling, pollution, the physical relocation of water basins through the erection of dams. . . .

It was a clear alarm gong, but its reverberations were quickly quelled in the din of bulldozers where they were reclaiming, developing and building vast projects like Glen Canyon Dam on the upper Colorado River. The Report to the President of the United States by the Committee on Natural Resources of the National Academy of Sciences—National Research Council, Publication 1000, became as extinct in three short years as the passenger pigeon. Let us see how extinct—even in the temple of science where they helped to frame that solemn document.*

Neither the 1962 Report of the Committee of Natural Resources, nor the Wilderness Act of 1964, has the slightest effect on the billion-dollar bureaus. Large staffs of indefatigable experts are hard at work in the offices of the Army Engineers and Bureau of Reclamation, not merely with Rampart, Glacier View, and Spruce Park Dams. Surely Grand Canyon National Park and Grand Canyon National Monument are safe? Not at all. Plans for Marble Canyon will locate a generating plant within sight of visitors to the Grand Canyon, and reduce the main flow of the river through the canyon to a mere trickle. Bridge Canyon Dam will, if built, impound water in Grand Canyon Monument and its reservoir will extend into the National Park (not for water conservation but to sell power to finance other Colorado River developments). It will submerge priceless geological records at the bottom of the canyon, and the drawdowns for power will stain the famous Inner Gorge walls.

The Bob Marshall Wilderness Area in the heart of the Rocky Mountains in Montana is being eyed by the Bureau of Reclamation as the site of a great reservoir to be created by two dams. (A former Secretary of the Interior had called off plans for drowning the marvelous wilderness by declaring that the Bob Marshall Wilderness Area "ranks among the half dozen finest unspoiled mountain wilderness tracts in the nation.") In Colorado's Flat Tops Primitive Area is another priceless American heritage. Plans are completed for a private electric generating plant that will

---

* In the January 8, 1965 issue, the Editor of *Science*, publication of the American Association for the Advancement of Science, urged consideration of a plan under study by a Senate subcommittee called NAWAPA (North American Water and Power Alliance). This proposes a series of dams, lifts, tunnels, canals, from the Yukon to the Columbia River, in order to create a reservoir 500 miles long in the wildest valleys of the Rocky Mountains, raise the level of the Great Lakes, and supply water to 33 states and Mexico, at a cost of 100 *billion* dollars.

flood the area. Such developments make a mockery of the National Wilderness Preservation Act of 1964.

As I am writing this book, water, that common commodity which Americans have generally taken for granted as a limitless resource of our generous continent, is making headlines in every corner of the land. *The National Observer* runs a full-page feature under the heading "The Shrinking Waterways—Falling Waterline Carries away Business and Fun on the Great Lakes." That same newspaper carries another full-page article about the falling water table in western Arizona near Lake Mead and a feature story on the parched Everglades National Park, Florida, due to Army Engineer water diversion projects. *The New York Times* reports how one by one the wells on Long Island are becoming brackish. "So much of western Long Island has been paved with highways, parking lots and driveways that rain water is diverted into streams instead of percolating into the ground."

A Columbia University forum notes that more than a thousand cities and towns in these United States already have been forced to curtail their water service. Near Chicago, where wells formerly flowed under their own pressure, new wells must go down 2 thousand feet to reach the water table. In Mississippi wells are now 400 feet deeper on the average than they were only ten years ago.

Glen Canyon Dam has had unplanned results. This great water-conservation project took seven years to build. It was supposed to solve the water problems of Arizona and supplement the great irrigation system centering on Lake Mead. It was built notwithstanding the doubt of geologists concerning its design, the warnings of hydrologists that water storage in reservoirs with a tremendous loss of water from surface evaporation is wasteful, and the predictions by power engineers that its electric production would be expensive and short-lived on the overdeveloped, silt-laden Colorado River.

In 1961 with the great Glen Canyon Dam only three years from closing its gates, the *Sierra Club Bulletin* viewed with alarm what was taking place: "The United States Bureau of Reclamation is destroying Glen Canyon needlessly ... a huge dam-building bureau, bent on self-perpetuation, can emit plausible-looking statistics and diagrams, can plant articles and hold press interviews faster than a true interpretation can overtake them." Cries of agony also centered on the threat to spectacular Rainbow Natural Bridge, an arch of salmon-pink sandstone "in surroundings unspoiled by man." So vast is the beautiful arch of Rainbow Bridge that it could span the Capitol at Washington if that could be placed under it.

In May 1964 Glen Canyon Dam closed its gates. But after a few months the water level of Lake Mead behind Hoover Dam, some 400 miles downstream on the Colorado, fell dangerously. The shrunken lake left the marina high and dry. In response to the howl for water from California, the President ordered Glen Canyon's gates reopened. It looks as though Arizona's irrigation from Glen Canyon will be unsatisfactory, to say the least, while Washington plays the water back and forth between the Hoover Dam and Glen Canyon Dam. The flow of the mighty Colorado has been greatly reduced, first by the cutting of forests in the Rocky Mountains around the headwaters of the Colorado River System, and then by great loss of water from evaporation from the surface of reservoirs.

Forest canopies are the finest and most efficient of water collectors and evaporation inhibitors. Their moist shade protects the ground from the direct rays of the sun and the water conserved outweighs by far the water released into the air by the transpiration of trees—water which. in any case, quickly returns to the forest as rain, snow and dew. Moreover, the undisturbed soil under trees permits the steady percolation of water into the water table. Brushland, swamp, and pasture are second only to forest as water collectors.

The issue is confused because of the great success of irrigation dams in arid country. Where the ground is bare in bright hot sun, dams collect much-needed water. In such country, irrigation canals tap running streams before they dump their water into the sea. These were successful, as were also local town and city reservoirs. *But that was when forested lands and grassy meadows covered an area greater than the concrete and man-changed land.* There was always a forest edge, always a mountain side, always a place just over there for hunting, fishing and a wood lot. Man's works were localized amid forest and grassy valley. *Today it is the forest and the moist earth that are localized.* Tremendous continental dams that drown thousands of square miles of forest and valley, that mutilate our continent's fertile moist humus, that alter continental river systems, may be a greater threat to man than bombs.

And yet the Bureaus do not pause. They burgeon under the sanctimonious banners of water conservation, reclamation, development. We pay our billions for Barmecides feasts.

If only people could catch a vision of the wonder of the American forests, especially people like the California highway commissioner, the New York State park commissioner, the engineers and planners of Senate subcommittees and the executives of the lumber and paper industries.

If only people would catch a vision of our fabulous forests, their ancient heritage, their beauty and beneficence, their meaning for our lives today . . . before it is too late.

Index

263